REVISE EDEXCEL AS
Mathematics
REVISION WORKBOOK

Series Consultant: Harry Smith
Author: Glyn Payne

Notes from the publisher

While the publishers have made every attempt to ensure that advice on the qualification and its assessment is accurate, the official specification and associated assessment guidance materials are the only authoritative source of information and should always be referred to for definitive guidance.

Pearson examiners have not contributed to any sections in this resource relevant to examination papers for which they have responsibility.

Also available to support your revision:

Revise A Level Revision Planner   9781292191546

The **Revise A Level Revision Planner** helps you to plan and organise your time, step-by-step, throughout your A level revision. Use this book and wall chart to mastermind your revision.

> **For the full range of Pearson revision titles across KS2, KS3, GCSE, Functional Skills, AS/A Level and BTEC visit:** www.pearsonschools.co.uk/revise

Contents

A small bit of small print

Edexcel publishes Sample Assessment Material and the Specification on its website. This is the official content and this book should be used in conjunction with it. The questions have been written to help you practise every topic in the book.

Index laws

1 Express $25^{-\frac{3}{2}}$ in the form 5^n **(2)**

....

Guided **2** Express $\sqrt{3}\left(27^{\frac{2}{3}}\right)$ in the form 3^x **(2)**

$\sqrt{3}\left(27^{\frac{2}{3}}\right) = 3^{\cdots} \times \left(27^{\cdots}\right)^2 = $ .... $= $ ....

3 Simplify $3x\left(2x^{-\frac{3}{4}}\right)$ **(2)**

....

4 Simplify $\dfrac{20x^{\frac{5}{3}}}{4x}$ **(2)**

....

Guided **5** Simplify fully $\dfrac{\left(3x^{\frac{1}{2}}\right)^3}{9x^3}$ **(3)**

$\dfrac{\left(3x^{\frac{1}{2}}\right)^3}{9x^3} = \dfrac{\cdots\cdots\cdots}{9x^3} = $ .... $= $ ....

> First simplify the numerator.

6 Write $\dfrac{3 - x^{\frac{3}{2}}}{\sqrt{x}}$ in the form $3x^p - x^q$ where p and q are constants. **(2)**

....

....

....

7 Solve $3^{2x+1} \times 9^x = 27$ **(2)**

....

....

....

> Write both sides of the equation as powers of 3 to find x.

8 Solve $2^{2x-3} \times 4^{x+2} = 8$ **(4)**

....

....

....

9 Write $\dfrac{6\sqrt{x} + 4x^{-\frac{3}{2}}}{2x^3}$ in the form $3x^p + 2x^q$ where p and q are constants. **(2)**

....

....

....

....

....

Expanding and factorising

> **Guided**   **1**   Expand $(x - 1)(x + 2)^2$ **(2)**

$(x - 1)(x + 2)^2 = (x - 1)(x^2 \dotfill)$

....

....

> First expand $(x + 2)^2$.

> Multiply out and collect like terms, then multiply by $(x - 1)$.

> **Guided**   **2**   Factorise completely $x^3 - 9x$ **(3)**

$x^3 - 9x = x(x^2 \dotfill)$

....

....

> First take out the common factor. Then factorise the expression inside the brackets.

3   Expand $(x - 4)(x + 2)(x - 1)$ **(2)**

....

....

....

4   Factorise completely $x^3 + 4x^2 - 5x$ **(3)**

....

....

....

5   Show that $(2 - 3\sqrt{x})^2$ can be written as $4 - k\sqrt{x} + 9x$ where k is a constant.   **(2)**

....

....

....

6   Given $f(x) = (x^2 - 4x)(x + 3) + 6x$

(a) express $f(x)$ in the form $x(ax^2 + bx + c)$ where a, b and c are constants.   **(3)**

....

....

....

(b) Hence factorise $f(x)$ completely.   **(2)**

....

....

Surds

1   Write $\sqrt{72}$ in the form $a\sqrt{2}$ where a is an integer.   **(2)**

....

 2   Simplify $\sqrt{18} + \sqrt{50}$, giving your answer in the form $a\sqrt{b}$ where a and b are integers.   **(2)**

$$\sqrt{18} + \sqrt{50} = \sqrt{9 \times 2} + \sqrt{25 \times 2}$$

$$= 3 \times \sqrt{2} + \text{.....................}$$

....

3   Simplify $\dfrac{\sqrt{5} + 3}{\sqrt{5} - 2}$ in the form $a + b\sqrt{5}$

where a and b are integers.   **(4)**

> Insert brackets and rationalise the denominator.

> Multiply out the brackets in the numerator and the denominator.

$$\frac{\sqrt{5} + 3}{\sqrt{5} - 2} = \frac{(\sqrt{5} + 3)(\sqrt{5} \text{.........})}{(\sqrt{5} - 2)(\sqrt{5} \text{.........})}$$

....

....

....

....

4   Express $\sqrt{75} + \dfrac{21}{\sqrt{3}}$ in the form $a\sqrt{3}$ where a is an integer.   **(3)**

....

> Rationalise the denominator in the second term.

....

....

5 $(9 + a\sqrt{2})(3 - \sqrt{2}) = 23 - b\sqrt{2}$ where a and b are integers.

Find the values of a and b.   **(4)**

....

....

6 $(c - \sqrt{3})^2 = d - 14\sqrt{3}$ where c and d are integers.

Find the values of c and d.   **(3)**

....

....

7   Write $\dfrac{3(2 - \sqrt{5})}{(2 + \sqrt{5})}$ in the form $a\sqrt{5} + b$ where a and b are integers.   **(5)**

....

....

....

Quadratic equations

1 Solve $3(x - 1)^2 + 8x - 11 = 0$ **(1)**

....

....

....

....

Guided **2** Given that $f(x) = x^2 - 10x + 15$

(a) express $f(x)$ in the form $(x + a)^2 + b$ where a and b are integers. **(3)**

$x^2 - 10x + 15 = (x \underline{\hspace{1cm}})^2 - \underline{\hspace{1cm}} + 15$

$\boxed{2a = -10}$

$= \underline{\hspace{4cm}}$

$\boxed{\text{Subtract } a^2.}$

....

(b) Hence, or otherwise, show that the roots of $x^2 - 10x + 15 = 0$ are $c \pm d\sqrt{10}$,
    where c and d are integers to be found. **(3)**

$(x \underline{\hspace{1cm}})^2 - \underline{\hspace{1cm}} = 0$

$\boxed{\text{Rearrange into completed square form then square root both sides.}}$

$(x \underline{\hspace{1cm}})^2 = \underline{\hspace{1cm}}$

$(x \underline{\hspace{1cm}}) = \underline{\hspace{1cm}}$

$\boxed{\text{Any positive number has two square roots.}}$

....

....

....

3 $8x - 6 - x^2 = q - (x + p)^2$ where p and q are integers. Find the values of p and q. **(3)**

....

....

$\boxed{\text{\textbf{Problem solving} Complete the square on the LHS or expand the RHS and equate coefficients.}}$

....

....

....

....

....

....

4 $3x^2 + 6x + 5 = a(x + b)^2 + c$ where a, b and c are integers. Find the values of a, b and c. **(3)**

....

$\boxed{\text{\textbf{Problem solving} Complete the square on the LHS or expand the RHS and equate coefficients.}}$

....

....

....

Functions and roots

Guided 1 Solve $2x^4 - x^2 - 28 = 0$ (4)

Let $u = x^2$, then $2u^2 - \text{..........} - \text{..........} = 0$, $(2u \text{..........})(u \text{..........}) = 0$

so $2u \text{..........} = 0$ or $u \text{..........} = 0$, giving $u = \text{..........}$ or $u = \text{..........}$

> Solve for u.

So using $u = x^2$, $x^2 = - \text{..........}$ but x^2 cannot be negative

so $x^2 = \text{..........}$, giving $x = \text{..........}$ and $x = \text{..........}$

2 Solve $63x^3 = 8 - 8x^6$ (4)

....

> Use $u = x^3$

....

....

....

....

3 Solve $2x - 13\sqrt{x} + 15 = 0$ (4)

....

> Use $u = \sqrt{x}$

....

....

....

....

....

4 Solve $x - 5\sqrt{x} = 24$ (4)

....

....

....

5 $f(x) = 4x^4 + 5x^2 - 6$ $x \in \mathbb{R}, x < 0$

Show that $f(x)$ has only one root and determine its exact value. (4)

....

....

....

6 Solve $x + 2\sqrt{x} = 7$, giving your answer in the form $a - b\sqrt{2}$ where a and b are integers to be found. (5)

....

....

....

....

....

Sketching quadratics

> **Guided** 1 Sketch the curve with equation $y = (x - 3)(x + 2)$, showing clearly the coordinates of any points where the curve crosses the coordinate axes. **(3)**

When $x = 0$, $y = (0 - 3)(0 + 2)$

　　　　　= ....

When $y = 0$, $0 = (x - 3)(x + 2)$

so　$x = $ .... or $x = $ ....

> **Guided** 2 Sketch the curve with equation $y = (x + 3)^2 + 4$, showing clearly the coordinates of any points where the curve crosses the coordinate axes. **(3)**

The coordinates of the vertex

are (............. , ...)

When $x = 0$, $y = (0 + 3)^2 + 4$

　　　　　= ....

> The curve with equation $y = (x + a)^2 + b$ has a **vertex** at $(-a, b)$.

3 Sketch the curve with equation $y = x(5 - x)$, showing clearly the coordinates of any points where the curve crosses the coordinate axes. **(3)**

....

....

....

....

....

4 $f(x) = 3x^2 - 12x + 17$

(a) Write $f(x)$ in the form $3(x - a)^2 + b$ where a and b are integers to be determined. **(3)**

....

....

(b) Sketch the graph of $y = f(x)$, labelling the minimum point and any points of intersection with the axes. **(3)**

....

....

....

....

....

(c) Use your graph to explain why the equation $3x^2 - 12x + 17 = 0$ has no real solutions. **(1)**

....

The discriminant

Guided 1 The equation $x^2 - 2px + p = 0$, where p is a non-zero constant, has equal roots.
   Find the value of p.   **(4)**

   $a = 1, b = -2p, c = $ ....

   > Identify the values of a, b and c.

   $b^2 - 4ac = (-2p)^2 - 4 \times 1 \times$ ....

   > **Problem solving** For equal roots $b^2 - 4ac = 0$.
   > Then solve to find p.

   ....

   ....

   ....

   ....

Guided 2 The equation $3x^2 + kx - 5 = k$ has no real solutions for x. Show that $k^2 + 12k + 60 < 0$ **(3)**

   $3x^2 + kx - 5$ .... $= 0$

   > Write in the form $ax^2 + bx + c = 0$ before
   > identifying the values of a, b and c.

   $a = 3, b = k, c = $ ....

   $b^2 - 4ac = (k)^2 - 4 \times 3 \times$ ....

   > **Problem solving** For no real roots
   > $b^2 - 4ac < 0$.

   ....

   ....

   ....

3 Find the value of the discriminant of $3x - 7 - x^2$ **(2)**

   ....

   ....

   ....

4 $f(x) = x^2 + (p - 4)x - 3p$ where p is a constant.

   (a) Find the discriminant of $f(x)$ in terms of p. **(2)**

   > **Problem solving** Complete the square of the
   > expression for the discriminant.
   > Show this will always be ≥ 0.

   ....

   ....

   (b) Show that the discriminant can be written in the form $(p + a)^2 + b$ where a and b are
       integers to be found.   **(2)**

   ....

   ....

   ....

   (c) Show that, for all values of p, the equation $f(x) = 0$ has distinct real roots.   **(2)**

   ....

   ....

   ....

7

Modelling with quadratics

Guided **1** A river cruise boat is sailing on a 60 km round trip.

It leaves the pier and sails 30 km upstream (against the current) before sailing back downstream (with the current) to the pier.

The total time for the trip is 3 hours.

The river flows at a speed of 5.5 km/h.

(a) Given that the speed of the boat in still water is u km/h, write down two expressions, in terms of u, for the times t_1 and t_2 of the journeys upstream and downstream respectively. **(3)**

Relative speed upstream = speed of boat − speed of current = ... km/h

Time to travel upstream, $t_1 = \dfrac{\text{distance}}{\text{relative speed}} = \dfrac{30}{..........}$ hours

Relative speed downstream = ... km/h

so $t_2 = \dfrac{\text{distance}}{\text{relative speed}} = \dfrac{30}{..........}$ hours

(b) Form an equation in u and rearrange it into the form $au^2 + bu + c = 0$ where a, b and c are numbers to be determined. **(3)**

$$\dfrac{30}{..........} + \dfrac{30}{..........} = 3$$

.... = ...

.... = ... so .... = 0

(c) By completing the square, or otherwise, determine the upstream speed of the boat. Hence find the values of t_1 and t_2 to the nearest minute. **(5)**

....

....

....

....

PROBLEM SOLVED! **2** A football is kicked from the ground at an angle of 32° above the horizontal with a speed of 27 m s^{-1}. Its height h above the ground at time t can be modelled by the equation $h = 14.3t - 5t^2$ where t represents the time it is in the air.

(a) For how long is the ball in the air? **(2)** When the ball hits the ground, $h = 0$

....

....

(b) By completing the square, or otherwise, determine the maximum height of the ball above the ground during its flight. **(4)**

.... Re-write the equation as $h = -5(t^2 - kt)$, where k is a constant.

....

....

....

Simultaneous equations

Guided   **1**   Solve the simultaneous equations

$$x - y = 3 \qquad ①$$
$$x^2 - 2y = 6 \qquad ②$$ **(7)**

> Number the equations to keep track of your working.

$$y = \text{.....................} \qquad ③$$

$$x^2 - 2(\text{.....................}) = 6$$

> Rearrange ① to write y in terms of x and substitute in ②.

$$\text{.................................} = 6$$

$$\text{.................................} = 0$$

> Solve the quadratic to find the two values of x.
> Substitute into ③ to find the corresponding values of y.

....

2   (a)   By eliminating y from the equations $y = x + 8$

$$xy + 3x^2 = 16$$

     show that $x^2 + 2x - 4 = 0$ **(2)**

....

....

   (b)   Hence, or otherwise, solve the simultaneous equations $y = x + 8$

$$xy + 3x^2 = 16$$

     giving your answers in the form $a \pm b\sqrt{5}$,   where a and b are integers.   **(5)**

....

....

....

3   The quadratic curve C has the equation $y = x^2 - 10x + 21$, and the line L has the equation $y = 5 - 2x$.

   (a)   Find the coordinates of any points of intersection of C and L.   **(5)**

....

....

....

....

   (b)   Sketch the graphs of C and L on the same axes
and explain how the sketch supports your
answer to part (a).   **(4)**

....

....

....

....

....

....

Inequalities

Guided **1** Find the set of values of x for which

(a) $2(x - 3) < 4 - 3x$ **(2)**

$2x - 6 < 4 - 3x$

> Expand the brackets and rearrange to make x the subject.

$5x < \ldots\ldots\ldots$ so $x < \ldots\ldots\ldots$

(b) $(2x - 5)(2 + x) < 0$ **(3)**

$(2x - 5)(2 + x) = 0$

> Make equal to zero and solve to find where the graph of $y = (2x - 5)(2 + x)$ crosses the x-axis.

So $x = \ldots\ldots\ldots$ or $x = \ldots\ldots\ldots$

$\ldots\ldots\ldots\ldots\ldots\ldots\ldots\ldots\ldots\ldots\ldots\ldots\ldots$

> Identify the range of values of x which makes $y < 0$.

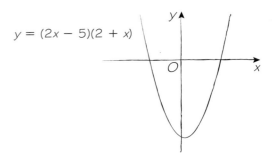

$y = (2x - 5)(2 + x)$

(c) both $2(x - 3) < 4 - 3x$ and $(2x - 5)(2 + x) < 0$

$\ldots\ldots\ldots < x < \ldots\ldots\ldots$

> The values where the inequalities **overlap** are the values which satisfy them both.

2 (a) Find the set of values of x for which $x^2 - 8x + 15 > 0$ **(3)**

$\ldots\ldots\ldots\ldots\ldots\ldots\ldots\ldots\ldots\ldots\ldots\ldots\ldots\ldots\ldots\ldots\ldots\ldots\ldots\ldots\ldots\ldots\ldots\ldots\ldots\ldots\ldots$

$\ldots\ldots\ldots\ldots\ldots\ldots\ldots\ldots\ldots\ldots\ldots\ldots\ldots\ldots\ldots\ldots\ldots\ldots\ldots\ldots\ldots\ldots\ldots\ldots\ldots\ldots\ldots$

(b) Sketch the curve with equation $y = x^2 - 8x + 15$.
Show on your sketch the coordinates at which the
curve meets the x-axis to illustrate your answer to
part (a). **(1)**

$\ldots\ldots\ldots\ldots\ldots\ldots\ldots\ldots\ldots\ldots\ldots\ldots\ldots\ldots\ldots\ldots\ldots\ldots\ldots\ldots$

$\ldots\ldots\ldots\ldots\ldots\ldots\ldots\ldots\ldots\ldots\ldots\ldots\ldots\ldots\ldots\ldots\ldots\ldots\ldots\ldots$

3 The equation $x^2 + 2kx + (3 - 2k) = 0$, where k is a constant, has different real roots.

(a) Show that $k^2 + 2k - 3 > 0$ **(2)**

$\ldots\ldots\ldots\ldots\ldots\ldots\ldots\ldots\ldots\ldots\ldots\ldots\ldots\ldots\ldots\ldots\ldots\ldots\ldots\ldots\ldots\ldots\ldots\ldots\ldots\ldots\ldots$

$\ldots\ldots\ldots\ldots\ldots\ldots\ldots\ldots\ldots\ldots\ldots\ldots\ldots\ldots\ldots\ldots\ldots\ldots\ldots\ldots\ldots\ldots\ldots\ldots\ldots\ldots\ldots$

(b) Find the set of possible values of k. **(3)**

$\ldots\ldots\ldots\ldots\ldots\ldots\ldots\ldots\ldots\ldots\ldots\ldots\ldots\ldots\ldots\ldots\ldots\ldots\ldots\ldots\ldots\ldots\ldots\ldots\ldots\ldots\ldots$

$\ldots\ldots\ldots\ldots\ldots\ldots\ldots\ldots\ldots\ldots\ldots\ldots\ldots\ldots\ldots\ldots\ldots\ldots\ldots\ldots\ldots\ldots\ldots\ldots\ldots\ldots\ldots$

4 Find the set of values of p for which the equation $x^2 - 2px - (p - 6) = 0$ has no real solutions. **(5)**

$\ldots\ldots\ldots\ldots\ldots\ldots\ldots\ldots\ldots\ldots\ldots\ldots\ldots\ldots\ldots\ldots\ldots\ldots\ldots\ldots\ldots\ldots\ldots\ldots\ldots\ldots\ldots$

$\ldots\ldots\ldots\ldots\ldots\ldots\ldots\ldots\ldots\ldots\ldots\ldots\ldots\ldots\ldots\ldots\ldots\ldots\ldots\ldots\ldots\ldots\ldots\ldots\ldots\ldots\ldots$

$\ldots\ldots\ldots\ldots\ldots\ldots\ldots\ldots\ldots\ldots\ldots\ldots\ldots\ldots\ldots\ldots\ldots\ldots\ldots\ldots\ldots\ldots\ldots\ldots\ldots\ldots\ldots$

Inequalities on graphs

Guided 1 (a) Sketch the graphs of $y = 2x^2 + 3x - 5$ and $y = 2x + 1$ on the same axes showing any points of intersection with the coordinate axes. **(4)**

$2x^2 + 3x - 5 = 0$, $(2x \,\rule{1cm}{0.15mm}\,)(x \,\rule{1cm}{0.15mm}\,) = 0$,

$x = \,\rule{1cm}{0.15mm}\,$ and $x = \,\rule{1cm}{0.15mm}\,$

When $x = 0$, $y = \,\rule{1cm}{0.15mm}\,$

For $y = 2x + 1$,
graph crosses y-axis when $x = 0$, so $y = \,\rule{1cm}{0.15mm}\,$

Graph crosses x-axis when $y = 0$, so $x = \,\rule{1cm}{0.15mm}\,$

(b) Determine the coordinates of the points of intersection of the two graphs. **(4)**

$2x^2 + 3x - 5 = 2x + 1$, $2x^2 \,\rule{2cm}{0.15mm}\, = 0$, $(2x \,\rule{1cm}{0.15mm}\,)(x \,\rule{1cm}{0.15mm}\,) = 0$,

$x = \,\rule{1cm}{0.15mm}\,$ and $x = \,\rule{1cm}{0.15mm}\,$

When $x = \,\rule{1cm}{0.15mm}\,$, $y = \,\rule{1cm}{0.15mm}\,$ and when $x = \,\rule{1cm}{0.15mm}\,$, $y = \,\rule{1cm}{0.15mm}\,$

(c) Solve the inequality $2x^2 + 3x - 5 \geqslant 2x + 1$ **(1)**

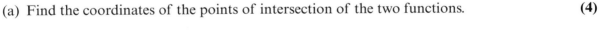

2 $f(x) = 6 - 5x - x^2$, $g(x) = -4 - 2x$

(a) Find the coordinates of the points of intersection of the two functions. **(4)**

(b) On the grid, draw the graphs of $y = f(x)$ and $y = g(x)$. Show the coordinates of the points at which the graphs meet the axes. **(4)**

(c) Solve the inequality $f(x) > g(x)$ **(1)**

(d) Shade the region on the graph that satisfies all of the following inequalities:

$y \leqslant f(x)$, $y \geqslant g(x)$, $x \leqslant -2$ **(2)**

Cubic and quartic graphs

Guided **1** The curve C has the equation $y = x(x + 2)(x - 5)$. Sketch C, showing clearly the coordinates of the points where the curve meets the coordinate axes. **(4)**

When $y = 0$, $0 = x(x + 2)(x - 5)$ so $x = $ .... or $x = $ .... or $x = $ ....

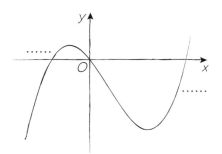

> The curve crosses the x-axis at the values of x which make each factor equal to 0.

> As x is a factor of $x(x + 2)(x - 5)$, the curve C will pass through the origin.

Guided **2** The curve C has the equation $y = (x + 1)^2(3 - x)$. Sketch C, showing clearly the coordinates of the points where the curve meets the coordinate axes. **(4)**

When $y = 0$, $0 = (x + 1)^2(3 - x)$ so $x = $ .... or $x = $ ....

When $x = 0$, $y = (0 + 1)^2(3 - 0) = $ ....

> As the factor $(x + 1)$ is repeated, the curve touches the x-axis at $x = -1$.

> Work out the point where the curve crosses the y-axis by setting $x = 0$.

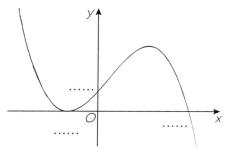

> As the coefficient of x^3 is negative, the shape of the curve will be 'upside down'.

3 The curve C has the equation $y = (x - 1)(x + 2)(x - 4)$. Sketch C, showing clearly the coordinates of the points where the curve meets the coordinate axes. **(4)**

....

....

....

4 Sketch the graph of $y = x(x + 4)(3x^2 - 11x + 6)$
Show clearly the coordinates of any intersections with the axes. **(4)**

....

....

....

Transformations 1

1 The diagram shows a sketch of a curve with equation $y = f(x)$. The curve has a maximum point at $(-2, 4)$ and a minimum point at $(0, 0)$.

On the same diagram, sketch the curve with equation

(a) $f(x - 2)$ **(3)**

> $f(x + a)$ is a translation of $f(x)$ by $\begin{pmatrix} -a \\ 0 \end{pmatrix}$

(b) $f(-x)$ **(3)**

> $f(-x)$ is a reflection of $f(x)$ in the y-axis.

On each sketch, show clearly the coordinates of the maximum and minimum points and any points of intersection with the axes.

2 The diagram shows a sketch of a curve with equation $y = f(x)$.
The curve has a minimum point at $(4, -16)$.

On separate diagrams, sketch the curve with equation

(a) $y = 3f(x)$ **(3)**

> $af(x)$ is a stretch, factor a, of $f(x)$ in the y-direction.

(b) $y = -f(x)$ **(3)**

> $-f(x)$ is a reflection of $f(x)$ in the x-axis.

(c) $y = f(2x)$ **(3)**

> $f(ax)$ is a stretch, factor $\frac{1}{a}$, of $f(x)$ in the x-direction.

On each sketch, show clearly the coordinates of the minimum point and any points of intersection with the axes.

The curve with equation $y = f(x + k)$ has a minimum point on the y-axis.

(d) What is the value of k? **(1)**

....

Transformations 2

1 The diagram shows a sketch of part of the curve with equation $y = f(x)$.

The curve has a minimum point $(2, -5)$ and an asymptote $y = -1$

On separate diagrams, sketch the curve with equation

(a) $y = f(x) + 3$ **(2)**

(b) $y = 3f(x)$ **(2)**

(c) $y = f(x - 1)$ **(3)**

On each diagram, show clearly the coordinates of the minimum point and the asymptote with its equation.

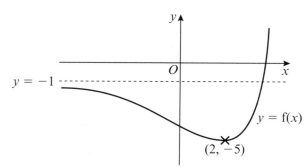

> The asymptote is horizontal so it is only transformed by a transformation in the y-direction.

2 The diagram shows a sketch of the curve with equation $y = f(x)$ where $f(x) = \dfrac{3x}{x - 1}$, $x \neq 1$

The curve has asymptotes with equations $y = 3$ and $x = 1$

(a) Sketch the curve with equation $y = f(x - 3)$ and state the equations of its asymptotes. **(3)**

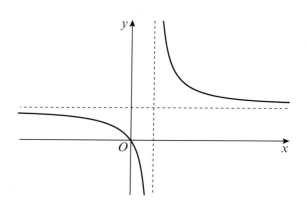

(b) Find the coordinates of the points where the curve with equation $y = f(x - 3)$ crosses the coordinate axes. **(3)**

....

....

....

Reciprocal graphs

1 The diagram shows a sketch of the curve with equation $y = \frac{4}{x}$, $x \neq 0$

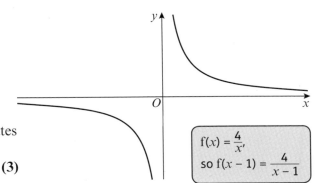

$f(x) = \frac{4}{x}$,
so $f(x - 1) = \frac{4}{x - 1}$

(a) On a separate diagram, sketch the curve with equation $y = \frac{4}{x - 1}$, $x \neq 1$, showing any asymptotes and the coordinates of any point at which the curve crosses a coordinate axis. **(3)**

(b) Write down the equations of the asymptotes of the curve in part (a). **(2)**

....

2 (a) Sketch the graph of $y = -\frac{8}{x^2}$, $x \neq 0$ **(2)**

Leave your answers in surd form where appropriate.

(b) On a separate diagram, sketch the graph of $y = -\frac{8}{x^2} + 4$, $x \neq 0$

Write down the equations of any asymptotes and the coordinates of any intersections of the graph with the axes. **(3)**

....

(c) On a separate diagram, sketch the graph of $y = -\frac{8}{(x - 2)^2}$, $x \neq 2$

Write down the equations of any asymptotes and the coordinates of any intersections of the graph with the axes. **(3)**

....

15

Points of intersection

Guided   **1**   The curve C has equation $y = -\dfrac{3}{x}$ and the line l has equation $x + y + 2 = 0$

(a) On the same axes, sketch the graphs of C and l, indicating clearly the coordinates of any intersections with the axes.   **(3)**

....

....

....

....

....

....

(b) Find the coordinates of the points of intersection of C and l.   **(6)**

$$y = -x - 2$$

$$-\frac{3}{x} = -x - 2$$

> Rearrange the linear equation to $y = -x - 2$.
> The x-coordinates at the points of intersection are the solutions to the equation $-\dfrac{3}{x} = -x - 2$.

....

....

....

....

2   (a) On the same axes, sketch the graphs of the curves with equation

(i) $y = x^2(x + 2)$

(ii) $y = x(4 - x)$

and indicate on your sketches the coordinates of all the points where the curves cross the x-axis.   **(6)**

....

....

....

....

....

(b) Use algebra to find the coordinates of the points where the graphs intersect.   **(7)**

....

....

....

....

....

....

Equations of lines

1   The line L has equation $y = 7 - 3x$

Show that the point $(3, -2)$ lies on L.   **(1)**

....

Guided   **2**   The line L has equation $2x + 7y - 3 = 0$

Find the gradient of L.   **(2)**

$7y =$ ....

$y =$ ....

Gradient = ...

> Rearrange the equation to make y the subject.

> The equation of a straight line can be written in the form $y = mx + c$, where m is the gradient of the line, and c is the point where it crosses the y-axis.

Guided   **3**   The line L passes through the point A $(3, -2)$ and has gradient $-\frac{1}{3}$

Find an equation of L, giving your answer in the form $y = mx + c$ **(3)**

$x_1 =$ .... $y_1 =$ .... $m =$ ....

$y -$ .... $=$ .... $(x -$ ....$)$

> If a straight line has gradient m and passes through the point (x_1, y_1), then you can write its equation as $y - y_1 = m(x - x_1)$.

> Remember to write the answer in the form asked for in the question.

....

....

Guided   **4**   The points A $(-2, 1)$ and B $(6, -2)$ lie on the line L.

(a) Find the gradient of the line L.   **(2)**

$x_1 =$ .... $y_1 =$ .... $x_2 =$ .... $y_2 =$ ....

$m = \dfrac{y_2 - y_1}{x_2 - x_1} =$

> If a straight line has gradient m and passes through the points (x_1, y_1) and (x_2, y_2), then $m = \dfrac{y_2 - y_1}{x_2 - x_1}$

(b) Find an equation for L in the form $ax + by + c = 0$, where a, b and c are integers.   **(2)**

....

....

....

5   (a) The line L has equation $3y = 4x + p$. The point A $(2, 3)$ lies on L.

Find the value of the constant p.   **(1)**

....

(b) Find an equation for the straight line joining the points A $(2, 3)$ and B $(-1, 7)$ in the form $ax + by + c = 0$, where a, b and c are integers.   **(4)**

....

....

....

....

Parallel and perpendicular

 1 The line L has equation $y = 4 - 3x$

(a) Show that the point P (3, −5) lies on L. **(1)**

....

(b) Find an equation of the line perpendicular to L, which passes through P.
Give your answer in the form $ax + by + c = 0$, where a, b and c are integers. **(4)**

> If the gradient of one line is a fraction, the gradient of a perpendicular line is found by turning the fraction upside down and changing the sign.

Gradient of L = ...

Gradient of perpendicular line = ...

Equation of perpendicular line through (3, −5) is ....

....

....

 2 The points P and Q have coordinates (−2, 5) and (6, 3) respectively.

(a) Find the coordinates of the midpoint of PQ. **(1)**

Coordinates of midpoint are

$$\left(\frac{-2 + 6}{2}, \frac{...............}{2}\right) = ...$$

> The coordinates of the midpoint of the line joining the points (x_1, y_1) and (x_2, y_2) are $\left(\frac{x_1 + x_2}{2}, \frac{y_1 + y_2}{2}\right)$.

(b) The line l is perpendicular to PQ and passes through the midpoint of PQ.
Find an equation for l, giving your answer in the form $ax + by + c = 0$, where a, b and c are integers. **(4)**

....

....

....

....

3 The line l_1 has equation $3x + 4y - 5 = 0$
The line l_2 is perpendicular to l_1 and passes through the point (1, 3).

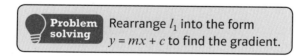

> **Problem solving** Rearrange l_1 into the form $y = mx + c$ to find the gradient.

Find the equation of l_2 in the form $y = mx + c$, where m and c are constants. **(5)**

....

....

....

....

Lengths and areas

1   A is the point $(-1, 6)$ and B is the point $(3, -2)$.
The length of AB is $p\sqrt{5}$, where p is an integer.
Find the value of p.   **(3)**

> Draw a sketch showing the positions of points A and B and use Pythagoras' theorem.

....

....

....

....

 2   The line l_1 has equation $y = x + 1$
The line l_2 has equation $x + 3y - 15 = 0$
l_1 and l_2 intersect at the point A.

(a) Find the coordinates of A.   **(3)**

$x + 3(x + 1) - 15 = 0$

$x + 3x +$ ....

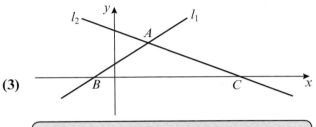

> Start by solving the equations simultaneously.

....

....

l_1 crosses the x-axis at the point B.
l_2 crosses the x-axis at the point C.

(b) Find the area of triangle ABC.   **(3)**

> Substitute $y = 0$ into the equations to find the x-coordinates of B and C, then use Area $= \frac{1}{2} \times$ base $\times$ height.

....

....

3   The line l_1 has equation $3x - 2y + 18 = 0$
The line l_2 is perpendicular to l_1 and passes through the point $(1, 4)$.
Find the area of the triangle formed by the lines l_1, l_2 and the x-axis.   **(9)**

....

....

....

....

....

....

....

....

....

....

Equation of a circle

1   A circle C has centre $(4, -1)$ and radius 6

    Write down the equation of the circle in the form $(x - a)^2 + (y - b)^2 = r^2$ **(2)**

....

Guided   **2**   The circle C has centre $(2, 3)$ and passes through the point $(-1, 7)$.

    (a)   Find an equation for C.   **(4)**

$r = \sqrt{(-1 - 2)^2 + (\underline{\quad} - \underline{\quad})^2} = \underline{\quad\quad\quad}$

       $(x\underline{\quad\quad})^2 + (y\underline{\quad\quad})^2 = r^2$

> First find r^2 using the formula for the distance between two points.

> Then find an equation for C using $(x - a)^2 + (y - b)^2 = r^2$ where (a, b) are the coordinates of the centre of C.

....

    (b)   Verify that the point $(5, 7)$ lies on C.   **(1)**

$(5\underline{\quad\quad})^2 + (7\underline{\quad\quad})^2 = \underline{\quad\quad\quad\quad\quad\quad}$

....

....

> Substitute $x = 5$ (and $y = 7$) into the left-hand side of the equation of the circle. Show all your working to verify that the expression is equal to $25 = 5^2$.

3   The points A and B have coordinates $(-3, 5)$ and $(5, 11)$ respectively.

    Given that AB is a diameter of the circle C, find an equation for C.   **(5)**

....

....

....

....

4.   The circle C has equation $x^2 + y^2 + 2x - 6y = 6$

    (a)   Find the centre and the radius of C.   **(5)**

> **Problem solving** First rearrange the formula, then complete the square to write it in the form $(x - a)^2 + (y - b)^2 = r^2$.

....

....

....

....

    (b)   Find the coordinates of the points where C crosses the coordinate axes, giving your answers as simplified surds.   **(6)**

....

....

....

....

....

....

Circle properties

1 The circle C has equation $x^2 + y^2 + 4x - 6y = 12$

The points P $(1, 7)$ and Q $(-5, -1)$ lie on the circle. Show that PQ is a diameter of C.   **(2)**

....

....

....

2 The line $5y = 3x + 32$ is a tangent to the circle C, touching C at the point P $(1, 7)$, as shown in the diagram. The point Q is the centre of C.

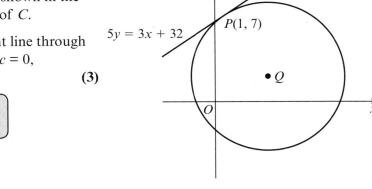

(a) Find an equation of the straight line through P and Q in the form $ax + by + c = 0$, where a, b and c are integers.   **(3)**

> The line through P and Q is **perpendicular** to the tangent.

Gradient of tangent = ...

Gradient of line through P and Q = ...

Equation of line is $y - y_1 = m(x - x_1)$

....

....

(b) Given that Q lies on the line $y = 2$, find the coordinates of Q.   **(1)**

....

3 A circle has equation $(x - 2)^2 + (y + 5)^2 = 180$

The tangent to the circle at the point $(8, 7)$ meets the x-axis at P and the y-axis at Q.

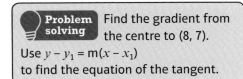

(a) Find the coordinates of P and Q.   **(5)**

....

....

....

....

....

....

(b) Find the area of the triangle PQC, where C is the centre of the circle.   **(4)**

....

....

....

....

Circles and lines

Guided   **1**   A circle has equation $(x + 3)^2 + (y + 2)^2 = 26$

A straight line has equation $y = 2x - 3$

The straight line intersects the circle twice.

Find the coordinates of the two points of intersection.   **(6)**

> Solve the equations simultaneously.

Substitute $y = 2x - 3$ into the equation of the circle.

$(x + 3)^2 + (2x - 3 + 2)^2 = 26 \Rightarrow (x + 3)^2 + (2x\dots\dots)^2 = 26$

$x^2 \dots\dots\dots\dots + 4x^2 \dots\dots\dots\dots = 26$

$5x^2 \dots\dots\dots\dots = 0$

$(5x\dots\dots)(x\dots\dots) = 0$, so $x = \dots\dots$ and $x = \dots\dots$

When $x = \dots\dots$, $y = 2 \times \dots\dots - 3 = \dots\dots$,

and when $x = \dots\dots$, $y = 2 \times \dots\dots - 3 = \dots\dots$

> Work out y for each of your values of x.

2   A circle has its centre at the point $(k, -1)$ and radius 4.

A straight line has equation $y = 2x - 1$

The circle and the straight line have no points of intersection.

 Problem solving   Write down the equation of the circle, solve the equations simultaneously, then use the discriminant of the resulting quadratic in x.

Find the range of possible values of k, giving your answer in surd form.   **(7)**

....

....

....

....

....

....

3   A circle has equation $x^2 + y^2 = 20$

A straight line has equation $3x - y + k = 0$, where k is a positive constant.

 Problem solving   Solve simultaneously. Use the discriminant of the resulting quadratic in x.

The straight line is a tangent to the circle.

Find the exact value of k.   **(7)**

....

....

....

....

....

....

....

The factor theorem

Guided **1** (a) Use the factor theorem to show that $(x + 2)$ is a factor of $2x^3 - 3x^2 - 11x + 6$ **(2)**

$f(x) = 2x^3 - 3x^2 - 11x + 6$

$f(\underline{\quad}) = 2(\underline{\quad})^3 - 3(\underline{\quad})^2 - 11(\underline{\quad}) + 6$

$= \text{..}$

$= \text{................}$

So $(x + 2)$ is a $\text{.....................}$

> Remember to write a conclusion or begin by stating, 'If $(x + 2)$ is a factor then $f(-2) = 0$.'

(b) Factorise $2x^3 - 3x^2 - 11x + 6$ completely. **(4)**

$f(x) = (x + 2)(2x^2 \text{............................})$

$= (x + 2)(2x \text{.............})(\text{.............})$

> $2x^3 - 3x^2 - 11x + 6 = (x + 2)(2x^2 - 7x + 3)$
> Use 'inspection':
> 1st term $2x^2$ to give $2x^3$, last term $+3$ to give $+6$
> A middle term of $-7x$ will give $4x^2 - 7x^2 = -3x^2$
> on the RHS, which is what we require.

2 Complete these factorisations:

(a) $2x^3 + 9x^2 - 20x - 12 = (x + 6)(\text{.....................}) = (x + 6)(\text{.............})(\text{.............})$ **(4)**

(b) $3x^3 - 10x^2 - 16x + 32 = (x - 4)(\text{.....................}) = (x - 4)(\text{.............})(\text{.............})$ **(4)**

(c) $6x^3 - 29x^2 + 36x - 9 = (x - 3)(\text{.....................}) = (x - 3)(\text{.............})(\text{.............})$ **(4)**

3 $f(x) = 2x^3 - x^2 - 22x + c$, where c is a constant.
Given that $f(4) = 0$

(a) find the value of c **(2)**

..

..

(b) factorise $f(x)$ completely. **(4)**

..

..

..

4 (a) Use the factor theorem to factorise $f(x) = 3x^3 + 8x^2 - 33x + 10$ **(5)**

..

..

..

..

> Test $f(1)$, $f(-1)$, $f(2)$, $f(-2)$ and so on, to find a linear factor.

(b) Find all the solutions of $f(x) = 0$ **(2)**

..

23

The binomial expansion

Guided 1 Find the first 3 terms, in ascending powers of x, of the binomial expansion of $(3 - 2x)^5$, giving each term in its simplest form. **(4)**

> The expansion for $(a + b)^n$ is
> $$a^n + \binom{n}{1}a^{n-1}b + \binom{n}{2}a^{n-2}b^2 + \ldots + b^n$$
> where $\binom{n}{r} = \dfrac{n!}{r!(n-r)!}$

$a =$ .... $b =$ .... $n =$ ....

$(3 - 2x)^5 = (3)^5 + \binom{5}{1}(3)^4($............$) +$ .... $+$ ....

$=$ ....

$\approx$ ....

> Remember to use brackets when substituting and be careful when substituting negative terms.

Guided 2 (a) Write down the first 3 terms, in ascending powers of x, of the binomial expansion of $(1 + px)^9$, where p is a non-zero constant. **(2)**

> Remember that $1^n = 1$.

$a =$ .... $b =$ .... $n =$ ....

$(1 + px)^9 = 1^9 +$ ....

$\approx$ ....

(b) Given that, in the expansion of $(1 + px)^9$, the coefficient of x is q and the coefficient of x^2 is $20q$, find the value of p and the value of q. **(4)**

$(1 + px)^9 =$ ....

> Solve the equations simultaneously to find the values of p and q.

.... $= q$　　.................... $= 20q$

....

....

3 Find the first 3 terms, in ascending powers of x, of the binomial expansion of $(4 - 3x)^7$ and simplify each term. **(4)**

....

....

....

4 (a) Find the first 3 terms, in ascending powers of x, of the binomial expansion of $(2 + 3x)^6$ **(4)**

....

....

....

....

(b) Hence, or otherwise, find the first 3 terms, in ascending powers of x, of the expansion of $\left(1 - \dfrac{x}{4}\right)(2 + 3x)^6$ **(3)**

....

....

....

....

Solving binomial problems

Guided 1 Find the coefficient of x^7 in the expansion of $\left(4 - \frac{x}{2}\right)^{12}$ (2)

> Use the formula for the general term given in the formulae booklet: $\binom{n}{r}a^{n-r}b^r$.

$n =$ .... $r =$ .... $a =$ .... $b =$ ....

$\binom{12}{.....}4^{.....}\left(-\frac{x}{2}\right)^{.....} =$ ....

....

Coefficient = ...

Guided 2 The first 4 terms of the expansion of $\left(1 + \frac{x}{2}\right)^8$ are given below:

$$\left(1 + \frac{x}{2}\right)^8 = 1 + 4x + 7x^2 + 7x^3 + \ldots$$

> Find the value of x to substitute in by solving $1 + \frac{x}{2} = 1.005$.

Use the expansion to estimate the value of $(1.005)^8$, giving your answer to 5 decimal places. (2)

$1 + \frac{x}{2} = 1.005, \ \frac{x}{2} =$ ...., $x =$ ....

$(1.005)^8 \approx 1 + 4(\underline{\hspace{1cm}}) + 7(\underline{\hspace{1cm}})^2 + 7(\underline{\hspace{1cm}})^3 \approx$ ....

3 (a) Find the first 4 terms of the binomial expansion, in ascending powers of x, of $\left(1 + \frac{x}{4}\right)^9$, giving each term in its simplest form. (4)

....

....

....

(b) Use your expansion to estimate the value of $(1.025)^9$, giving your answer to 4 decimal places. (3)

....

....

4 (a) Find the first 4 terms, in ascending powers of x, of the binomial expansion of $(1 - 2x)^7$ Give each term in its simplest form. (4)

....

....

....

(b) Use your expansion to estimate the value of $(0.98)^7$, giving your answer to 4 decimal places. (3)

....

....

(c) If x is small, so that x^3 and higher powers can be ignored, show that
$$\left(1 - \frac{x}{2}\right)(1 - 2x)^7 \approx 1 - \frac{29}{2}x + 91x^2$$ (2)

....

....

....

....

Proof

Guided **1** The nth term of a sequence is $\dfrac{n}{n+1}$

(a) Write down the $(n+1)$th term. **(1)**

$(n+1)$th term $= \dfrac{n+1}{\text{............}}$

(b) Prove that the difference between the $(n+1)$th term and the nth term is $\dfrac{1}{(n+1)(n+2)}$

> Subtract the algebraic fractions and simplify.

Difference $= \dfrac{(n+1)}{(\text{.........})} - \dfrac{n}{(n+1)} = \dfrac{\text{.....................}}{(\text{.........})(\text{.........})} = \dfrac{\text{.....................}}{(\text{.........})(\text{.........})}$

(c) Which two terms have a difference of $\dfrac{1}{156}$? **(1)**

....

2 Prove that the difference between the cubes of two consecutive odd numbers is 2 greater than 6 times the square of the mean of the two consecutive odd numbers.

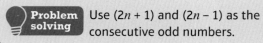

> **Problem solving** Use $(2n+1)$ and $(2n-1)$ as the consecutive odd numbers. **(6)**

....

....

....

....

....

....

....

....

3 (a) Prove by exhaustion that $2n^2 - n + 1$ is not divisible by 11 for $1 \leqslant n \leqslant 7$ **(2)**

....

....

(b) By means of a counter example, disprove the statement:

"If n is prime, then $n^2 + 3n + 1$ will always be prime." **(2)**

....

....

4 Prove that, when n is even, the value of $3n^2 + 6n$ is always divisible by 12

> **Problem solving** Factorise, then use the fact that n is even.

.... **(3)**

....

....

....

Cosine rule

Guided 1 In the triangle ABC, $AB = 8$ cm, $AC = 5$ cm and $\angle BAC = 122°$.
Find the length of BC to 3 significant figures. **(3)**

Sketch the triangle and label the sides a, b and c. You know two sides and the angle between them, so use the cosine rule.

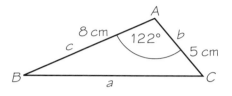

$a^2 = b^2 + c^2 - 2bc\cos A$

$a^2 = 5^2 +$ ....^{2} $- 2 \times$ .... $\times$ .... $\times \cos 122° =$ ....

$a =$ .... cm

Guided 2 In the triangle ABC, $AB = 6$ cm, $AC = 12$ cm and $BC = 9$ cm. Find the size of angle B, giving your answer to 3 significant figures. **(3)**

Sketch the triangle and label the sides a, b and c. You know all three sides so use the cosine rule.

$\cos B = \dfrac{a^2 + c^2 - b^2}{2ac}$

$= \dfrac{9^2 + ...^2 - .....^2}{2 \times ..... \times .....} =$ ....

$B = \cos^{-1}($ .... $) =$ ....

3 The diagram shows a lighthouse at O and two boats, one at P and one at Q. Boat P is 600 m due north of the lighthouse at O and boat Q is 900 m from O. The bearing of Q from O is 025°. Calculate the distance between boat P and boat Q, in metres, to 3 significant figures. **(3)**

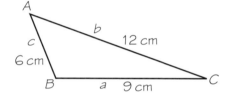

....

....

....

....

4 A car drives 18 km from P to Q on a bearing of 123°.
It then changes direction and drives 26 km from Q to R on a bearing of 345°.
Find the distance of R from P, giving your answer to 3 significant figures. **(4)**

....

....

....

....

....

....

....

Sine rule

> **Guided**   **1**   In the triangle ABC, $AC = 9\,cm$, $\angle BAC = 53°$ and $\angle ACB = 59°$.
> Find the length of AB to 3 significant figures.   **(3)**

Not SAS or SSS so use the sine rule.

$\angle ABC = 180° - 53° - 59° = \,.............$

$\dfrac{b}{\sin B} = \dfrac{c}{\sin C} \qquad \dfrac{.....}{\sin ....} = \dfrac{c}{\sin ....}$

$so \; c = \dfrac{.....\sin ....}{\sin ....} = \,.............\, cm \; (3 \; s.f.)$

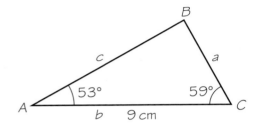

> **Guided**   **2**   In the triangle PQR, $PQ = 14\,cm$, $PR = 8\,cm$, $\angle PQR = 18°$ and $\angle PRQ = x°$.

(a) Use the sine rule to find the value of $\sin x$, giving your answer to 4 decimal places.   **(3)**

Use the alternative form of the sine rule when working out an angle.

$\dfrac{\sin x}{.....} = \dfrac{\sin .....}{.....} \qquad \sin x = \dfrac{.....\sin .....}{.....} = \,.............$

(b) Given that there are two possible values of x, find these values of x, giving your answers to 1 decimal place.   **(3)**

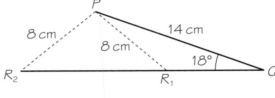

This is known as the ambiguous case of the sine rule.

$x = \sin^{-1}(\,............) = \,............ \qquad or \qquad x = 180° - (\,............) = \,............$

3   In the diagram, $AB = 8.3\,cm$, $AD = 19.4\,cm$
$\angle ABC = 110°$, $\angle ACB = 26°$ and $\angle ADC = 52°$

(a) Find the length of AC.   **(3)**

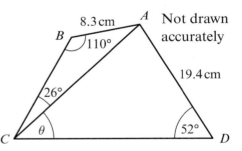

....

....

(b) Find the angle ACD, marked θ on the diagram.   **(3)**

....

....

(c) Work out the area of the quadrilateral $ABCD$.
   Give your answer to 3 significant figures.   **(6)**

....

....

....

....

Trigonometric graphs

1 (a) Sketch, for $0 \leqslant x \leqslant 360°$, the graph of $y = 3\cos x$ **(2)**

(b) Write down the coordinates of the maximum and minimum points.   **(2)**

....

> **Guided**

2 (a) Sketch, for $0 \leqslant x \leqslant 360°$, the graph of $y = \sin(x - 60°)$ **(2)**

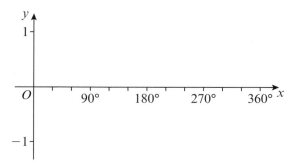

> The graph of $y = \sin(x - 60°)$ is a translation of the graph of $y = \sin x$ by $\begin{pmatrix} 60° \\ 0 \end{pmatrix}$

(b) Write down the exact coordinates of the points where the graph meets the coordinate axes.   **(3)**

> You should know the exact values of sin, cos and tan of 30°, 45° and 60°.

When $x = 0$: $y = \sin(0 - 60°)$, $= -\sin(60°) = $ ....

Meets y-axis at $(0,$ ....$)$

When $y = 0$, $x = $ .... and $x = $ ....

Meets x-axis at $($ ....$, 0)$ and $($ ....$, 0)$

3 The diagram shows part of the curve with equation $y = \cos(ax + b)$, where $a > 0$ and $0 < b < 180°$

The curve cuts the x-axis at the points P and Q.

P is the point $(40°, 0)$ and Q is the point $(160°, 0)$.

Find the values of a and b.   **(4)**

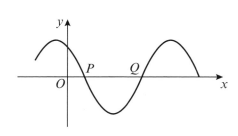

....

....

....

....

> The graph of $y = \cos x$ crosses the x-axis at 90°, 270°, etc.

> Write down two equations and solve them simultaneously to find a and b.

....

....

Trigonometric equations 1

Guided 1 Solve $5 \sin x = 2$ in the interval $0 \leqslant x \leqslant 360°$, giving your answers to 1 decimal place. **(3)**

> Draw a sketch of $y = \sin x$ for the range given in the question. This will tell you the number of solutions there are within the range.

> Check your calculator is in degrees mode and work out $\sin^{-1}\left(\frac{2}{5}\right)$ to find the **principal value** of x.

> To find the second value of x, work out $180° -$ (principal value).

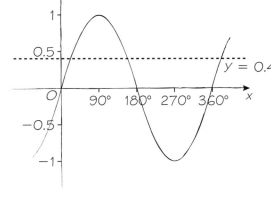

$\sin x = \dfrac{2}{5} = 0.4$

$x = \sin^{-1}(0.4) = $ ....   or $x = 180° - $ .... $ = $ ....

Guided 2 Solve $\tan x = 3$ in the interval $0 \leqslant x \leqslant 360°$, giving your answers to 1 decimal place. **(3)**

$\tan x = 3$

$x = \tan^{-1}(3) = $ ....

or $x = 180° + $ .... $ = $ ....

You can use a CAST diagram to answer this question.

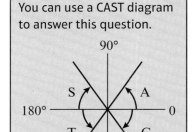

3 (a) Sketch the graph of $y = \cos x$ in the interval $0 \leqslant x \leqslant 360°$. **(2)**

(b) Find the values of x in the interval $0 \leqslant x \leqslant 360°$ for which $\cos x = -0.2$, giving your answers correct to 1 decimal place. **(3)**

....

....

4 Solve the following equations in the interval $-180° \leqslant x \leqslant 180°$, giving your answers to 1 decimal place.

Problem solving Sketching graphs will help.

(a) $5 \sin x + 3 = 0$ **(3)**

....

....

....

(b) $3 \cos x = 2$ **(3)**

....

....

....

Trigonometric identities

Guided

1 (a) Show that the equation $3\sin x = 2\cos^2 x$ can be written in the form $2\sin^2 x + 3\sin x - 2 = 0$ **(2)**

> Write everything in terms of $\sin^2 x$ and $\sin x$ by using $\sin^2 x + \cos^2 x = 1$.

$3\sin x = 2\cos^2 x$ $\sin^2 x + \cos^2 x = 1$ so $\cos^2 x = ...$

$3\sin x = 2(........................)$

....

(b) Hence solve, for $0 \leqslant x < 360°$, $3\sin x = 2\cos^2 x$ **(4)**

$2\sin^2 x + 3\sin x - 2 = 0$

$(2\sin x ....)(\sin x ....) = 0$

$\sin x = ...$

$x = ...$ or $x = ...$

> Factorise the quadratic to find solutions for $\sin x$. Remember that $-1 \leqslant \sin x \leqslant 1$, so only one of the factors will give you solutions.

Guided

2 (a) Given that $2\cos\theta = 3\sin\theta$, find the value of $\tan\theta$.   **(1)**

$\dfrac{\sin\theta}{\cos\theta} = \dfrac{............}{............}$ $\tan\theta = ...$

> Rearrange the equation to find $\dfrac{\sin\theta}{\cos\theta} = \tan\theta$.

(b) Hence, or otherwise, find the values of θ in the interval $0 \leqslant \theta < 360°$ for which $2\cos\theta = 3\sin\theta$, giving your answers to 1 decimal place.   **(3)**

> Find $\tan^{-1}\theta$. Remember that there are two solutions in the range.

$\theta = \tan^{-1}(............)$

$\theta = ...$ or $\theta = ...$

3 Find all the solutions, in the interval $0 \leqslant \theta \leqslant 360°$, of the equation $(1 - \tan\theta)(2\sin\theta + 1) = 0$ **(4)**

Problem solving   Equate each of the factors to zero.

....

....

....

....

4 Find all solutions in the interval $0 \leqslant \theta \leqslant 360°$ of the equation $10\sin^2\theta + \cos\theta - 8 = 0$, giving your answers to 1 decimal place.   **(7)**

Problem solving   Write as a quadratic equation in $\cos\theta$.

....

....

....

....

....

....

....

....

Trigonometric equations 2

Guided   **1** Solve, for $0 \leqslant x \leqslant 180°$, the equations

(a) $\sin 2x = \frac{1}{2}$ **(4)**

$0 \leqslant 2x \leqslant$ ....°   Let $Z = 2x$

$\qquad Z = \sin^{-1}\left(\frac{1}{2}\right) =$ ....

or $\quad Z = 180° -$ .... $=$ ....

$2x =$ .... or ....

$\quad x =$ .... or ....

> The range for $2x$ is twice the range for x.

> You should know $\sin 30° = \cos 60° = \frac{1}{2}$

> The sketch shows that there are two solutions of $\sin 2x = \frac{1}{2}$ for $0 \leqslant x \leqslant 180°$.

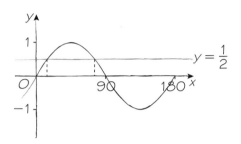

(b) $\cos(x - 50°) = 0.3$, giving your answers to 1 decimal place.   **(4)**

............° $\leqslant x - 50° \leqslant$ ....°   Let $Z = x - 50°$

$Z = \cos^{-1}(0.3) =$ .... or $Z = 360° -$ .... $=$ ....

$x - 50° =$ .... , $x =$ ....

> You must work out the range for $(x - 50°)$

> Check that your solutions for x lie within the given range.

2 Solve, for $-180° \leqslant x < 180°$, $\tan(x + 45°) = 2.5$, giving your answers to 1 decimal place.   **(3)**

....

....

....

....

3 Find all the values of θ, to 1 decimal place, in the interval $0 \leqslant \theta < 360°$ for which $4\sin(\theta + 10°) = 3$ **(4)**

....

....

....

4 Find the exact values of θ in the interval $0° \leqslant \theta < 360°$ for which $\tan^2(\theta - 78°) = 3$

> **Problem solving** $\tan(\theta - 78°) = \pm\sqrt{3}$ Consider positive and negative solutions separately.   **(6)**

....

....

....

....

....

....

....

Vectors

Guided 1 The points P and Q have position vectors $\mathbf{i} + 7\mathbf{j}$ and $3\mathbf{i} + 2\mathbf{j}$ respectively.

(a) Find $\left|\overrightarrow{OP}\right|$ **(1)**

$\left|\overrightarrow{OP}\right| = \sqrt{1^2 + 7^2} = \sqrt{1 + \ldots\ldots\ldots\ldots} = \sqrt{\ldots\ldots\ldots\ldots} = \ldots\ldots\ldots$

(b) Find the vector $\overrightarrow{QP}$.   **(2)**

$\overrightarrow{OP} = \overrightarrow{QO} + \overrightarrow{OP} = \overrightarrow{OP} - \overrightarrow{OQ}$

> The position vectors $\overrightarrow{OP}$ and $\overrightarrow{OQ}$ could be written in the form $\begin{pmatrix} 1 \\ 7 \end{pmatrix}$ and $\begin{pmatrix} 3 \\ 2 \end{pmatrix}$ respectively.

$= \underset{\sim}{\mathbf{i}} + 7\underset{\sim}{\mathbf{j}} - (3\underset{\sim}{\mathbf{i}} + 2\underset{\sim}{\mathbf{j}}) = \ldots\ldots\ldots\ldots$

(c) Find the distance QP.   **(2)**

....

2 Find unit vectors in the direction of

(a) $8\mathbf{i} - 6\mathbf{j}$ **(1)**   (b) $8\mathbf{i} + 15\mathbf{j}$ **(1)**   (c) $12\mathbf{i} - 5\mathbf{j}$ **(1)**

....

....

3 For each pair of position vectors $\overrightarrow{OP}$ and $\overrightarrow{OQ}$, find (i) vector $\overrightarrow{PQ}$ (ii) $\left|\overrightarrow{PQ}\right|$

(a) $\overrightarrow{OP} = 4\mathbf{i} + 3\mathbf{j}$ and $\overrightarrow{OQ} = \mathbf{i} - 2\mathbf{j}$ **(3)**   (b) $\overrightarrow{OP} = 3\mathbf{i} + 5\mathbf{j}$ and $\overrightarrow{OQ} = -6\mathbf{i} - 8\mathbf{j}$ **(3)**

....

....

4 $\overrightarrow{OR} = \lambda\mathbf{i} - 2\lambda\mathbf{j}$ where λ is a constant.

Given that $\left|\overrightarrow{OR}\right| = 10$, find the possible values of λ.   **(4)**

....

....

5 $\overrightarrow{OP} = \mathbf{i} + \mu\mathbf{j}$, $\overrightarrow{OQ} = -3\mu\mathbf{i} + \mathbf{j}$, μ is a constant.

Given that $\left|\overrightarrow{QP}\right| = 5\sqrt{2}$, find the possible values of μ.   **(7)**

....

....

....

....

....

Solving vector problems

Guided 1 Points A, B and C have position vectors $\begin{pmatrix} -2 \\ 5 \end{pmatrix}$, $\begin{pmatrix} 4 \\ 2 \end{pmatrix}$ and $\begin{pmatrix} 6 \\ 4 \end{pmatrix}$ respectively.

(a) Find the vectors $\overrightarrow{AB}$, $\overrightarrow{BC}$ and $\overrightarrow{AC}$. **(3)**

$$\overrightarrow{AB} = \overrightarrow{AO} + \overrightarrow{OB} = \overrightarrow{OB} - \overrightarrow{OA} = \begin{pmatrix} 4 \\ 2 \end{pmatrix} - \begin{pmatrix} -2 \\ 5 \end{pmatrix} = \begin{pmatrix} \cdots \\ \cdots \end{pmatrix}$$

$$\overrightarrow{BC} = \overrightarrow{BO} + \overrightarrow{OC} = \overrightarrow{OC} - \overrightarrow{OB} = \begin{pmatrix} \cdots \\ \cdots \end{pmatrix} - \begin{pmatrix} \cdots \\ \cdots \end{pmatrix} = \begin{pmatrix} \cdots \\ \cdots \end{pmatrix}$$

$$\overrightarrow{AC} = \overrightarrow{AO} + \overrightarrow{OC} = \text{...................} = \text{...................}$$

(b) Find the area of triangle ABC. **(4)**

$$\left| \overrightarrow{AB} \right| = \sqrt{6^2 + (-3)^2} = \sqrt{45}$$

....

....

....

....

....

....

> 1 Use Pythagoras to find the length of all three sides of the triangle.
> 2 Use the cosine rule to find the size of one angle.
> 3 Use Area $= \frac{1}{2}ab \sin C$ to find the area of the triangle.

Point D is such that $ABCD$ is a parallelogram.

(c) Write down the area of the parallelogram. **(1)**

....

(d) Find the position vector of D. **(2)**

> Sketch a diagram showing the points A, B, C and D and use direction vectors to find the position vector of D.

2 The diagram shows a triangle OAB. OBR is a straight line.

$$\overrightarrow{OA} = 4\mathbf{a}, \quad \overrightarrow{OB} = 5\mathbf{b}, \quad \overrightarrow{BR} = \mathbf{b}$$

$OP : PA = 3 : 1$ and $AQ : QB = 2 : 1$

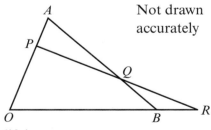

Not drawn accurately

(a) Find each of these vectors in terms of $\mathbf{a}$ and $\mathbf{b}$, simplifying your answers,

(i) $\overrightarrow{AB}$ **(1)** (ii) $\overrightarrow{PQ}$ **(3)**

....

....

....

(b) Prove that points P, Q and R are collinear. **(3)**

....

....

Differentiating from first principles

Guided   **1**   Prove, from first principles, that the derivative of $x^3 + 5x^2$ is $3x^2 + 10x$ **(4)**

$f(x) = x^3 + 5x^2$

$f'(x) = \lim\limits_{h \to 0} \dfrac{f(x + h) - f(x)}{h}$

$\quad = \lim\limits_{h \to 0} \dfrac{(x + h)^3 + 5(x + h)^2 - x^3 - 5x^2}{h}$

$\quad = \lim\limits_{h \to 0} \dfrac{x^3 + 3x^2h + \text{............} + \text{............} + 5x^2 + \text{............} + \text{............} - \text{............} - 5x^2}{h}$

$\quad = \lim\limits_{h \to 0} \dfrac{3x^2h + \text{..}}{h}$

$\quad = \lim\limits_{h \to 0} 3x^2 \text{...}$

As $h \to 0$, $\text{...................................}$ so $f'(x) = 3x^2 + 10x$ as required.

2   Points P and Q, with x-coordinates 3 and $3 + h$ respectively, lie on the curve $y = 2x^2 - 7x + 1$

Use differentiation from first principles to find the gradient of the tangent to the curve at point P.   **(4)**

....

....

....

....

....

....

....

....

3 $f(x) = ax^2 + 3bx$ where a and b are constants. Prove, from first principles, that $f'(x) = 2ax + 3b$.   **(4)**

....

....

....

....

....

....

....

Differentiation 1

1   The curve C has equation $y = 5x - 3x^{\frac{3}{2}} + 4x^3$, $x > 0$
    Find an expression for $\dfrac{dy}{dx}$ (3)

> If $y = ax^n$, then $\dfrac{dy}{dx} = anx^{n-1}$.

....

....

Guided 2   Given $y = 5x^2 + \dfrac{2}{x} - \dfrac{3}{x^2}$, $x \neq 0$, find $\dfrac{dy}{dx}$ (3)

> Write every term in the polynomial in the form ax^n before differentiating.

$y = 5x^2 + 2x^{\cdots\cdots} - 3x^{\cdots\cdots}$

$\dfrac{dy}{dx} = $ ....

Guided 3   Differentiate $\dfrac{3x - 2\sqrt{x}}{x}$, $x \neq 0$, with respect to x.   (3)

> Divide each term by x and write in the form ax^n before differentiating. Remember that $\sqrt{x} = x^{\frac{1}{2}}$.

$f(x) = \dfrac{3x - 2\sqrt{x}}{x} = \dfrac{3x}{x} - \dfrac{2\sqrt{x}}{x} = $ ....

> Constant terms differentiate to zero.

$f'(x) = $ ....

....

4   (a) Write $\dfrac{5x^{\frac{1}{3}} - 2}{x}$ in the form $5x^p - 2x^q$, where p and q are constants.   (2)

....

....

Given that $y = 4x - 9 + \dfrac{5x^{\frac{1}{3}} - 2}{x}$, $x > 0$

(b) find $\dfrac{dy}{dx}$ (4)

....

....

....

....

5   Given $f(x) = \dfrac{(4 + \sqrt{x})^2}{x}$, $x \neq 0$, find $f'(x)$.   (4)

> Multiply out the brackets then simplify before differentiating.

....

....

....

....

....

....

Differentiation 2

1   Given that $y = 4x^3 - 3x + 5$, find

(a) $\dfrac{\mathrm{d}y}{\mathrm{d}x}$ **(3)**

....

(b) $\dfrac{\mathrm{d}^2y}{\mathrm{d}x^2}$ **(1)**

> Differentiate twice to find the second derivative $\dfrac{\mathrm{d}^2y}{\mathrm{d}x^2}$ (or $\mathrm{f}''(x)$).

....

  2   The curve C has equation $y = 5x - \dfrac{2}{x^2}$, $x \neq 0$

The point P has coordinates $(1, 3)$.

(a) Show that P lies on C.   **(1)**

....

(b) Find the gradient of the curve at P.   **(2)**

$y = 5x - \dfrac{2}{x^2} = 5x - 2x^{\cdots\cdots}$

$\dfrac{dy}{dx} = $ ....

> $\dfrac{\mathrm{d}y}{\mathrm{d}x}$ represents the gradient of the curve C at any point. To find the gradient at P, substitute $x = 1$.

When $x = 1$, $\dfrac{dy}{dx} = $ ....   Gradient at $P = $ ....

3 $\mathrm{f}(x) = 3x - \dfrac{4}{x}$

(a) Find $\mathrm{f}'(x)$.   **(2)**

....

Given that $\mathrm{f}'(x) = 12$

(b) find the possible values of x.   **(3)**

....

....

....

4   A curve, C, has equation $y = x^3 + x^2 - 12x$

(a) Find the points where C meets the x-axis, and sketch the curve.   **(5)**

....

....

....

(b) Find $\dfrac{\mathrm{d}y}{\mathrm{d}x}$ **(2)**

....

(c) Find the gradient of C at each of the points where the curve meets the x-axis.   **(3)**

....

....

Tangents and normals

Guided **1** The curve C has equation $y = \frac{1}{3}x^3 + 2x^2 - 8x + 4$

The point P with coordinates $(3, 7)$ lies on C. Find an equation of the tangent to C at P, giving your answer in the form $y = mx + c$, where m and c are constants. **(5)**

> The gradient of a curve at any point is the same as the gradient of the tangent to the curve at that point.

$y = \frac{1}{3}x^3 + 2x^2 - 8x + 4$

$\frac{dy}{dx} = $ ....

When $x = 3$, $\frac{dy}{dx} = $ ....

> Find the value of $\frac{dy}{dx}$ at P, then use $y - y_1 = m(x - x_1)$ to find the equation of the tangent.

Equation of tangent: $y - $ ...... $ = $ ...... $(x - $ ......$)$

....

Guided **2** The curve C has equation $y = 8x + 2x^{\frac{3}{2}} - 3x^2$, $x > 0$

(a) Show that the point $P\,(4, 0)$ lies on C. **(1)**

....

(b) Find an expression for $\frac{dy}{dx}$ **(3)**

....

(c) Find an equation of the normal to C at the point P, giving your answer in the form $ax + by + c = 0$, where a, b and c are integers. **(6)**

> The normal to the curve at P is a straight line that is perpendicular to the tangent.

$\frac{dy}{dx} = $ ....

When $x = 4$, $\frac{dy}{dx} = $ ....

Gradient of tangent $= $ ...... so gradient of normal $= $ ......

Equation of normal: $y - $ .... $ = $ .... $(x - $ ....$)$

> Write the gradient of the tangent as a fraction. Find the gradient of the normal by turning the fraction upside down and changing the sign.

....

3 The curve C has equation $y = (x + 2)(x^2 - 9)$

(a) Show that $\frac{dy}{dx} = 3x^2 + 4x - 9$ **(3)**

....

....

(b) Show that $y = 6x + 18$ is an equation of the tangent to C at the point $(-3, 0)$. **(2)**

....

....

The tangent to C at the point R is parallel to the tangent at the point $(-3, 0)$.

(c) Find the exact x-coordinate of R. **(3)**

....

....

....

Stationary points 1

Guided   1   Find the coordinates of the stationary point on the curve with equation $y = 3x^2 - 18x$ **(4)**

$$\frac{dy}{dx} = \text{.........}x - 18$$

$$\text{.........}x - 18 = 0$$

$$x = \text{............} \Rightarrow y = \text{.........................}$$

> At a **stationary** point or **turning** point $\frac{dy}{dx} = 0$.

> Solve the equation to find x, then substitute the x-value into the equation for y.

Guided   2   The diagram shows part of the curve with equation

$$y = 18 - 5x - \frac{20}{x^2}$$

Use calculus to show that y is decreasing for $x > 2$ **(4)**

$y = 18 - 5x - 20x^{-2}$

$\dfrac{dy}{dx} = -5\text{.....................} = -5\text{.....................}$

If $x > 2$, then $x^3 > \text{.............}$ and $\text{.............} < 5$

So $\text{.........................} < 0$ and hence y is decreasing.

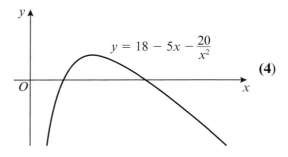

> If y is decreasing, then $\frac{dy}{dx} \leqslant 0$

3   Find the coordinates of the stationary point on the curve with equation $y = 2x^2 - 8x + 5$ **(4)**

....

....

4   Find the coordinates of the turning points on the curve with equation $y = x^3 - 7x^2 - 5x + 6$ **(6)**

> There are **two** turning points on this curve. Differentiate first, then solve the quadratic equation by factorising.

....

....

....

....

5   A curve has equation $f(x) = 27x^2 - \dfrac{16}{x} - 45$

The function is decreasing for $x < k$, where k is a number to be found.

Use calculus to find the value of k.

> Investigate $f'(x) = 0$

   (5)

....

....

....

....

Stationary points 2

Guided **1** The curve C has equation $y = x^3 + 3x^2 - 24x$

(a) Use calculus to find the coordinates of the stationary points. **(6)**

$\dfrac{dy}{dx} = 3x^2$ .... , $\dfrac{dy}{dx} = 0$ when $3x^2$ .... $= 0$

$3(x^2$ ....$) = 0$, $3(x$............)$(x$............$) = 0$, $x =$ .... and $x =$ ....

When $x =$ .... , $y =$ .... and when $x =$ .... , $y =$ ....

(b) Find $\dfrac{d^2y}{dx^2}$ and hence verify the nature of the stationary points. **(3)**

$\dfrac{d^2y}{dx^2} = 6x$ .... When $x =$ .... $\dfrac{d^2y}{dx^2} =$ .... , so we have a ....

When $x =$ .... $\dfrac{d^2y}{dx^2} =$ .... , so we have a ....

2 The curve C has equation $y = 8 - 2x - \dfrac{6}{x^3},\ x \neq 0$

(a) Use calculus to find the exact values of the x-coordinates of the stationary points. **(5)**

....

....

....

....

(b) Find $\dfrac{d^2y}{dx^2}$ and hence verify the nature of the stationary points. **(3)**

....

....

3 Sketch the graph of $y = f'(x)$ on the axes below each of the curves $y = f(x)$.

(a)
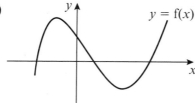

(b)
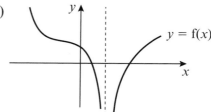

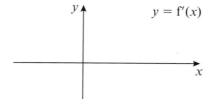

(4)

(4)

Modelling with calculus

1 The diagram shows an open-topped cardboard box, in the shape of a cuboid. The base of the box is a rectangle x centimetres by $2x$ centimetres. The height of the box is y centimetres. The volume of the box is 8000 cm³.

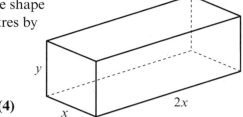

(a) Show that the area, A cm², of the cardboard used to make the box is given by $A = \dfrac{24\,000}{x} + 2x^2$ **(4)**

Volume = $2x^2y = 8000$

$y = \dfrac{8000}{\ldots\ldots\ldots} = \ldots\ldots\ldots$ $A = \ldots\ldots\ldots\ldots\ldots\ldots\ldots\ldots$

....

....

....

> First find an equation connecting x and y using the formula for the volume of the cuboid, then write y in terms of x. Simplify your answer.

> Work out an expression for A in terms of x, remembering that the box is open topped.

(b) Use calculus to find the value of x for which A is stationary, correct to 3 s.f. **(4)**

....

....

....

....

> Differentiate the expression for A and put equal to 0, then solve to find the value of x which gives a stationary value.

(c) Prove that this value of x gives a minimum value of A. **(2)**

....

....

> Find $\dfrac{d^2A}{dx^2}$ and substitute the value of x. Remember to write a statement to say what your answer shows.

(d) Calculate the minimum area of cardboard needed to make the box. **(2)**

....

....

> Substitute the value of x into the equation for A to find the area of cardboard needed.

PROBLEM SOLVED!

2 A solid right circular cylinder has radius r cm and height h cm as shown in the diagram. The total surface area of the cylinder is 900 cm².

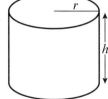

(a) Show that the volume, V cm³, of the cylinder is given by
$V = 450r - \pi r^3$ **(4)**

....

....

....

(b) Given that r varies, use calculus to find the maximum value of V, to the nearest cm³. **(6)**

....

....

....

(c) Justify that the value of V you have found is a maximum. **(2)**

....

....

Integration

Guided 1 Given that $y = 4x - \dfrac{3}{x^2}$, $x \neq 0$, find $\int y\,dx$ **(3)**

> Write every term in the polynomial in the form ax^n before integrating.

$y = 4x - 3x^{-2}$

$\int y\,dx = \dfrac{4x^{\cdots}}{\cdots} \cdots$

> $\int ax^n\,dx = \dfrac{ax^{n+1}}{n+1} + c$ where c is a constant.

....

Guided 2 Find $\int(3x^2 - 5 + x^{-\frac{1}{2}})\,dx$, giving each term in its simplest form. **(4)**

> Dividing by $\dfrac{a}{b}$ is the same as multiplying by $\dfrac{b}{a}$

$\int(3x^2 - 5 + x^{-\frac{1}{2}})\,dx = \dfrac{3x^3}{\cdots} - \cdots$

....

....

3 Find $\int \dfrac{6x - 3}{2x^3}\,dx$ **(4)**

> Write as two separate fractions then integrate each term.

....

....

....

....

4 (a) Show that $(3 - 2\sqrt{x})^2$ can be written in the form $9 - k\sqrt{x} + 4x$, where k is a constant to be found. **(2)**

....

....

(b) Find $\int(3 - 2\sqrt{x})^2\,dx$ **(3)**

....

....

....

5 Given that $\dfrac{4x^2 - 2x^{\frac{5}{2}}}{\sqrt{x}}$ can be written in the form $4x^p - 2x^q$

(a) write down the value of p and the value of q. **(2)**

....

....

(b) Find $\int \dfrac{4x^2 - 2x^{\frac{5}{2}}}{\sqrt{x}}\,dx$ **(3)**

....

....

....

....

Finding the constant

> **Guided**   **1**   The curve C with equation $y = f(x)$, $x \neq 0$, passes through the point $(2, 10)$.

Given that $f'(x) = 3x + \dfrac{2}{x^2}$

(a) find $f(x)$ **(5)**

> To find $f(x)$ you need to integrate $f'(x)$.

> To find the constant of integration, use $f(x) = 10$ when $x = 2$.

$f(x) = \int\left(3x + \dfrac{2}{x^2}\right) dx$

$\quad = \int(3x + 2x^{\cdots\cdots}) \, dx$

$\quad = \text{.....................} + c$

$\quad = \text{...}$

$10 = \text{.....................} + c$

$\;c = \text{............}$

$f(x) = \text{...}$

(b) verify that $f(-1) = 8.5$ **(1)**

> To find $f(-1)$ substitute $x = -1$ into the equation for $f(x)$.

$\quad f(x) = \text{...}$

$f(-1) = \text{...} = \text{............}$

> **Guided**   **2**   The gradient of a curve C is given by $\dfrac{dy}{dx} = \dfrac{x - 3}{\sqrt{x}}$, $x \neq 0$

The point $(4, \frac{1}{3})$ lies on C. Find y in terms of x.   **(6)**

> To find y you need to integrate $\dfrac{dy}{dx}$

$\dfrac{dy}{dx} = \dfrac{x - 3}{\sqrt{x}} = x^{\cdots\cdots} - 3x^{\cdots\cdots}$

$y = \int(x^{\cdots\cdots} - 3x^{\cdots\cdots}) \, dx = \text{.....................} + c$

> To find the constant of integration, use $y = \frac{1}{3}$ when $x = 4$.

$\dfrac{1}{3} = \text{...} + c$

$\dfrac{1}{3} = \text{...}$

$c = \text{...}$

$y = \text{...}$

3   The gradient of a curve C is given by $\dfrac{dy}{dx} = \dfrac{(x^2 - 2)^2}{x^2}$, $x \neq 0$

(a) Show that $\dfrac{dy}{dx} = x^2 - 4 + 4x^{-2}$ **(2)**

....

....

The point $(3, \frac{2}{3})$ lies on C.

(b) Find an equation for the curve C in the form $y = f(x)$.   **(6)**

....

....

....

....

....

....

Definite integration

Guided   1   Use calculus to find $\int_1^2 (x^3 - 3x^2 + 5x - 7)\,dx$ **(4)**

$$\int_1^2 (x^3 - 3x^2 + 5x - 7)\,dx = \left[\frac{x^{\cdots\cdots}}{\cdots\cdots} - x^3 + \cdots\cdots\cdots\cdots\cdots\cdots\cdots\cdots\cdots\cdots\right]_1^2$$

$$= (\cdots\cdots\cdots\cdots\cdots\cdots\cdots) - (\cdots\cdots\cdots\cdots\cdots\cdots\cdots)$$

$$= \cdots\cdots\cdots - \cdots\cdots\cdots\cdots = \cdots\cdots\cdots\cdots$$

Guided   2   Use calculus to find the exact value of $\int_1^2 \left(2x^2 + 3 - \frac{5}{x^2}\right)dx$ **(5)**

$$\int_1^2 \left(2x^2 + 3 - \frac{5}{x^2}\right)dx = \int_1^2 (2x^2 + 3 - 5x^{\cdots\cdots})\,dx$$

$$= \left[\frac{2x^{\cdots\cdots}}{\cdots\cdots} + 3\cdots\cdots\cdots\cdots\cdots\right]_1^2 = \left[\cdots\cdots\cdots\cdots\cdots\cdots\cdots\right]_1^2$$

$$= (\cdots\cdots\cdots\cdots\cdots\cdots\cdots) - (\cdots\cdots\cdots\cdots\cdots\cdots\cdots)$$

$$= \cdots\cdots\cdots - \cdots\cdots\cdots\cdots = \cdots\cdots\cdots\cdots$$

> Write every term in the polynomial in the form ax^n before integrating.

3   Use calculus to find the value of $\int_1^4 (5x - 3\sqrt{x})\,dx$ **(5)**

> Dividing by $\frac{a}{b}$ is the same as multiplying by $\frac{b}{a}$

....

....

....

....

....

4   Evaluate $\int_2^8 \left(x + \frac{2}{\sqrt{x}}\right)dx$, giving your answer in the form $a + b\sqrt{2}$,

where a and b are integers.   **(5)**

....

....

....

....

....

5   Use calculus to find the exact value of $\int_1^2 \left(\frac{3}{x^4} - \frac{2}{x^3} + 5\right)dx$ **(5)**

....

....

....

....

....

Area under a curve

Guided   **1**   The diagram shows part of the curve with equation $y = (x + 1)(3 - x)$

Use calculus to find the exact area of the shaded region, R.   **(5)**

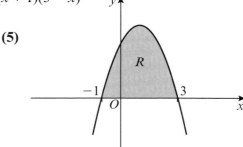

> Expand the brackets then integrate with limits of -1 and 3.

Graph crosses x-axis at $x = -1$ and $x = 3$

$y = 3 + 2x - x^2$

$$\int_{-1}^{3}\left(3 + 2x - x^2\right)dx = \Big[\dots\dots\dots\dots\dots\dots\Big]^{3} = \Big[\dots\dots\dots\dots\dots\dots\Big]_{-1}^{3}$$

$= (\dots\dots\dots\dots\dots\dots) - (\dots\dots\dots\dots\dots\dots) = \dots\dots\dots - \dots\dots\dots\dots = \dots\dots\dots\dots$

Area $= \dots\dots\dots$

Guided   **2**   The diagram shows part of the curve with equation
$y = (x + 2)(x - 4)$

Find the area of the shaded region, R.   **(5)**

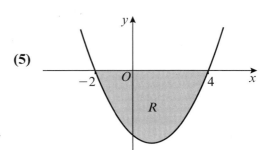

> Remember to write the **positive** value as your answer.

Graph crosses x-axis at $x = \dots\dots\dots$ and $x = \dots\dots\dots$

$y = \dots\dots\dots\dots\dots\dots\dots\dots$

$$\int_{\dots}^{\dots}\left(\dots\dots\dots\dots\dots\dots\right)dx = \Big[\dots\dots\dots\dots\dots\dots\Big]_{\dots}^{\dots} = \Big[\dots\dots\dots\dots\dots\dots\Big]_{\dots}^{\dots}$$

$= (\dots\dots\dots\dots\dots\dots) - (\dots\dots\dots\dots\dots\dots) = \dots\dots\dots\dots\dots\dots\dots\dots = \dots\dots\dots\dots\dots$

Area $= \dots\dots\dots$

3   The diagram shows part of the curve C with
equation $y = x(x - 2)(x - 6)$

Use calculus to find the total area of the finite
region, shown shaded in the diagram, that is
between $x = 0$ and $x = 4$ and is bounded by C,
the x-axis and the line $x = 4$ **(9)**

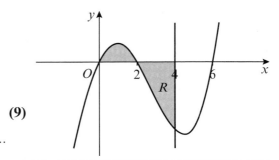

> **Problem solving** You need to work out two
> separate integrals and add
> the areas together, because an area below
> the x-axis will produce a **negative** integral.

$\dots\dots\dots\dots\dots\dots\dots\dots\dots\dots\dots\dots\dots\dots\dots\dots\dots\dots\dots\dots\dots\dots\dots\dots\dots\dots\dots\dots$

$\dots\dots\dots\dots\dots\dots\dots\dots\dots\dots\dots\dots\dots\dots\dots\dots\dots\dots\dots\dots\dots\dots\dots\dots\dots\dots\dots\dots$

$\dots\dots\dots\dots\dots\dots\dots\dots\dots\dots\dots\dots\dots\dots\dots\dots\dots\dots\dots\dots\dots\dots\dots\dots\dots\dots\dots\dots$

$\dots\dots\dots\dots\dots\dots\dots\dots\dots\dots\dots\dots\dots\dots\dots\dots\dots\dots\dots\dots\dots\dots\dots\dots\dots\dots\dots\dots$

$\dots\dots\dots\dots\dots\dots\dots\dots\dots\dots\dots\dots\dots\dots\dots\dots\dots\dots\dots\dots\dots\dots\dots\dots\dots\dots\dots\dots$

$\dots\dots\dots\dots\dots\dots\dots\dots\dots\dots\dots\dots\dots\dots\dots\dots\dots\dots\dots\dots\dots\dots\dots\dots\dots\dots\dots\dots$

$\dots\dots\dots\dots\dots\dots\dots\dots\dots\dots\dots\dots\dots\dots\dots\dots\dots\dots\dots\dots\dots\dots\dots\dots\dots\dots\dots\dots$

$\dots\dots\dots\dots\dots\dots\dots\dots\dots\dots\dots\dots\dots\dots\dots\dots\dots\dots\dots\dots\dots\dots\dots\dots\dots\dots\dots\dots$

More areas

> **Guided** **1** The diagram shows part of the curve C with
equation $y = x^2 - 6x + 8$

The points L and M have coordinates (2, 0) and
(4, 0) respectively. The point N lies on the curve
and has x-coordinate 6. The shaded region R is
bounded by the curve, the x-axis and the line
segment LN. Find the exact area of R.   **(7)**

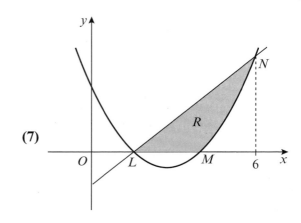

> You need to find the area of the triangle
> and the area under C between $x = 4$ and
> $x = 6$ then subtract to find R.

L (2, O); M (4, O)   At N: $x = 6$, $y =$ ....

Area of a triangle $= \frac{1}{2} \times$ base $\times$ height $= \frac{1}{2} \times$ .... $\times$ ....

$\int_4^6 \left(x^2 - 6x + 8\right) dx = \left[\dfrac{x^3}{3} - \text{.............} + \text{.............}\right]_4^6 = \left[\text{...........................}\right]_4^6$

$\qquad = (\text{............} - \text{............} + \text{............}) - (\text{............} - \text{............} + \text{............})$

$\qquad = \text{...........................} - \text{...........................} = \text{...........................}$

Area of $R =$ .... $-$ .... $=$ ....

2 The line with equation $y = 20 - 3x$ cuts the
curve with equation $y = x^2 + 2x + 14$ at the
points A and B, as shown in the diagram.

(a) Use algebra to find the coordinates of A
and the coordinates of B.   **(5)**

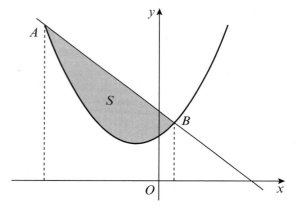

....

....

....

....

....

The shaded region S is bounded by the line and the curve, as shown in the diagram.

(b) Use calculus to find the exact area of S.   **(7)**

....

....

....

....

> **Problem solving** Find the area of the trapezium
> and the area under the curve
> between A and B.
> Area of $S =$ area of trapezium $-$ area under C

....

....

....

....

Exponential functions

1 Match each function to one of the graphs below.

(a) $y = \left(\frac{1}{4}\right)^x$ **(1)** (b) $y = 3^x - 4$ **(1)** (c) $y = 0.6^x - 1$ **(1)** (d) $y = -(5^{-x})$ **(1)**

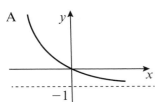 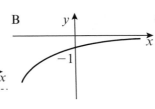 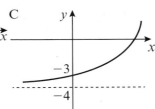 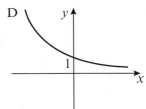

> **Guided** **2** Sketch these graphs.

(a) $y = -1 - (0.5)^x$ **(3)**

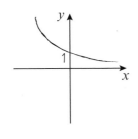 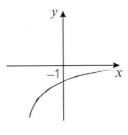 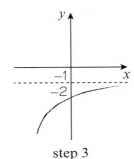

step 1   step 2   step 3

Step 1: draw $y = 0.5^x$
Step 2: reflect it in the x-axis.
Step 3: translate it by $\begin{pmatrix} 0 \\ -1 \end{pmatrix}$

(b) $y = 3^{x+2}$ **(3)** (c) $y = 4^{x-1} + 2$ **(3)** (d) $y = 4 - (0.8)^x$ **(3)**

3 Differentiate with respect to x.

(a) $y = e^{6x}$ **(1)** (b) $y = e^{-3x}$ **(1)** (c) $y = 4e^{\frac{x}{2}}$ **(1)** (d) $y = 6e^{0.2x}$ **(1)**

....

(e) $y = 7e^{-x} - 2e^{-4x}$ **(2)** (f) $y = e^{-2x}(3e^{5x} - 1)$ **(3)** (g) $y = e^{\frac{x}{4}}(e^x + 2e^{2x})$ **(3)**

....

....

Logarithms

Guided 1 (a) Write down the value of $\log_8 64$ **(1)**

$8^{\cdots} = 64$ so $\log_8 64 = \cdots$

(b) Express $3\log_a 2 + \log_a 7$ as a single logarithm to base a. **(3)**

$3\log_a 2 = \log_a 2^{\cdots} = \log_a \cdots$

$\log_a \cdots + \log_a 7 = \log_a (\cdots \times \cdots) = \log_a \cdots$

> Use $\log_a (x^n) = n\log_a x$ and
> $\log_a x + \log_a y = \log_a (xy)$.

2 Find

(a) the value of p such that $\log_4 p = -2$ **(2)**

(b) the value of y such that $\log_y 125 = 3$ **(2)**

3 Express as a single logarithm to base a

(a) $2\log_a 5 + 3\log_a 2$ **(2)**

(b) $4\log_a 3 - \log_a 12$ **(2)**

Guided 4 Given that $y = 4x^3$, show that $\log_4 y = 1 + 3\log_4 x$ **(3)**

$\log_4 y = \log_4 4x^3$

$= \log_4 \cdots + \log_4 \cdots$

$= \cdots + \cdots \log_4 \cdots$

> Take logs on both sides, then use $\log_a m + \log_a n = \log_a (mn)$
> to write as the sum of two separate log terms.

> Remember that $\log_a a = 1$.

5 Given that $y^2 = 9x^4$, show that $\log_3 y = 1 + 2\log_3 x$ **(3)**

> **Problem solving** Take logs to base 3 on both sides

6 Write $\log_a \left(\dfrac{x^3 \sqrt{y}}{z^4} \right)$ in terms of $\log_a x$, $\log_a y$ and $\log_a z$ **(3)**

Equations with logs

Guided 1 Find the value of x for which $\log_3(2x - 1) - \log_3 x = 1$ **(4)**

$$\log_3\left(\frac{\text{......................}}{\text{......................}}\right) = 1$$

$$\frac{\text{......................}}{\text{......................}} = 3^{\text{.....}}$$

....

....

> Use $\log_a m - \log_a n = \log_a\left(\frac{m}{n}\right)$ to combine the two log expressions on the left-hand side.

> Use $\log_a b = n \Leftrightarrow a^n = b$, then rearrange the equation to solve for x.

2 Solve the equation $\log_2(x + 2) - \log_2 x = \log_2 5$ **(3)**

....

....

Guided 3 Given that a and b are positive constants, solve the simultaneous equations

$$a = 4b \qquad \text{①}$$
$$\log_2 a + \log_2 b = 3 \qquad \text{②}$$

> Substitute ① into ②.

Give your answers as exact numbers.   **(6)**

$$\log_2 \text{......} + \log_2 b = 3$$

....

....

....

> Combine the log terms and apply $\log_a b = x \Leftrightarrow a^x = b$.

> Remember that a and b are **positive** and give **exact** values.

4 (a) Given that $2\log_2(x - 2) - \log_2(6 - x) = 1$, show that $x^2 - 2x - 8 = 0$ **(5)**

....

....

....

....

....

(b) Hence, or otherwise, solve $2\log_2(x - 2) - \log_2(6 - x) = 1$ **(2)**

> Remember that $\log_a b$ is only defined for $b > 0$.

....

....

....

5 Find the values of x such that $\dfrac{\log_3 81 + \log_3 243}{\log_3 x} = \log_3 x$ **(5)**

....

....

....

....

....

Exponential equations

> **Guided**

1 (a) Find, to 3 significant figures, the value of x for which $3^x = 5$ **(2)**

$$3^x = 5$$

$$\log 3^x = \log 5$$

> Take logs on both sides or make use of the log∎☐ key.

$$x \log 3 = \log 5$$

$$x = \frac{\cdots\cdots\cdots}{\cdots\cdots\cdots} = \cdots\cdots\cdots\cdots$$

> Rearrange the equation to find x. Then use the log key.

(b) Solve the equation $3^{2x} - 8(3^x) + 15 = 0$ **(4)**

Let $Y = 3^x$ so $3^{2x} = (3^x)^2 = Y^{\cdots}$

> Let $Y = 3^x$ then write as a quadratic in Y and factorise.

$$Y^2 - 8Y + 15 = 0$$

$$(Y\cdots\cdots)(Y\cdots\cdots) = 0$$

$Y = \cdots\cdots$ or $Y = \cdots\cdots$ so $3^x = \cdots\cdots$ or $3^x = \cdots\cdots$

$x = \cdots\cdots$ or $x = \cdots\cdots$

> Use $a^x = b \Leftrightarrow \log_a b = x$ to find the values of x.

2 Solve the equation $5^{2x} + 3(5^x) - 10 = 0$, giving your answer to 2 decimal places. **(6)**

> Remember that $a^x > 0$.

....

....

3 Solve the equation $8^{2x} - 8(8^x) + 7 = 0$ **(6)**

....

....

....

4 Solve, giving answers to 3 decimal places,

(a) $4^x = 3^{x+2}$ **(4)**

(b) $6^{2x-1} = 5^{x+1}$ **(4)**

> **Problem solving** Take logs to the same base on both sides, then use the power law.
> Collect all the x terms on one side of the equation, then factorise to get x on its own.

....

....

....

....

5 $f(x) = 3^{0.5x^2}$, $x \in \mathbb{R}$ and $g(x) = 9^{x-1}$, $x \in \mathbb{R}$

Show that the curves $f(x)$ and $g(x)$ meet at exactly one point. **(5)**

> **Problem solving** Set $f(x) = g(x)$ then take logs of both sides.
> Use the discriminant of the resulting quadratic in x.

....

....

....

Natural logarithms

Guided   **1** Solve $\ln(5x + 24) = 2\ln(x + 2)$ **(4)**

$\ln(5x + 24) = \ln(x + 2)^2$

$5x + 24 = (x + 2)^2$

> Rearrange as a quadratic in x, factorise and solve. Check the validity of your answers.

....

....

2 Solve $\ln(x - 3) + \ln(x - 2) = \ln(2x + 24)$ **(5)**

....

....

3 Find the exact solutions of
$$e^{3x} + 2e^x = 3e^{2x}$$ **(5)**

 Problem solving Write e^{3x} as $(e^x)^3$ and e^{2x} as $(e^x)^2$. Take all terms to the LHS then take out e^x as a common factor. You will have a quadratic in e^x as the other factor.

....

....

....

....

4 Solve $3^x e^{2x-1} = 5$

Give your answers in the form $\dfrac{\ln a + b}{\ln c + d}$

where a, b, c and d are integers.   **(5)**

 Problem solving Take logs of both sides, then use the laws of logs to simplify the LHS. Group the x-terms together.

....

....

....

5 The function f is defined by
$$f : x \mapsto \frac{5x^2 - 13x - 6}{x^2 - 9}, \qquad x > 3$$

(a) Show that $f(x) = \dfrac{5x + 2}{x + 3}$ **(3)**

....

....

(b) Hence, or otherwise, solve the equation $\ln(5x^2 - 13x - 6) = 2 + \ln(x^2 - 9)$, $x > 3$, giving your answer in terms of e.   **(4)**

....

....

....

....

Exponential modelling

Guided

1 A heated metal bar is put in a liquid. The temperature of the bar, $T°C$, at time t minutes is modelled by the equation

$$T = 350\,e^{-0.08t} + 20, \qquad t \geq 0$$

(a) Write down the temperature of the bar as it enters the liquid. **(1)**

....

(b) Find t when $T = 280$, giving your answer to 3 s.f. **(4)**

$280 = 350\,e^{-0.08t}$ so $\dfrac{260}{350} = e^{-0.08t}$ so $\ln\left(\dfrac{260}{350}\right) = -0.08t$

....

(c) Find the rate at which the temperature is decreasing at time $t = 40$. Give your answer in °C/minute to 3 s.f. **(3)**

> Differentiate to find the rate of change.

....

....

(d) Explain why the temperature can never fall to $18\,°C$. **(1)**

....

2 A sample of radioactive material decays according to the formula $N = 60\,e^{-kt}$ where N is the number of grams of the material, t is the time, in years, and k is a positive constant.

(a) What was the initial mass of the sample? **(1)**

....

After 88 years, the sample has lost half its mass.

(b) Find the value of k to 3 significant figures. **(4)**

....

....

(c) How many grams of material are there after 120 years? **(2)**

....

(d) Find the rate of decay, in grams per year, after 50 years. Give your answer to 3 s.f. **(2)**

....

....

(e) Sketch a graph of N against t. **(2)**

Modelling with logs

Guided 1 The percentage of people visiting the theatre, P, has increased steadily since 1990.
It can be represented by the equation $P = at^n$, where t is the number of years after 1990 and a and n are constants to be determined.

(a) Show that the graph of $\log_{10} P$ against $\log_{10} t$ will be a straight line of gradient n. **(2)**

$\log_{10}P = \log_{10}(at^n) = \log_{10}a + \log_{10}t^n = \log_{10}a + \underline{\quad\quad}\log_{10}\underline{\quad\quad}$

(b) Write down, in terms of a, the intercept of this graph on the vertical axis. **(1)**

Intercept = ...

(c) This sketch graph shows the relationship between t and P.
Use it to work out the equation for P in terms of t. **(4)**

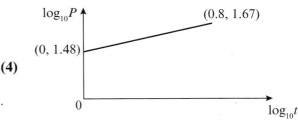

$n = \text{gradient} = \dfrac{1.67 - 1.48}{0.8} = $ ....

Intercept $= 1.48 = \log_{10}a$, so $a = $ ....

So the equation is $P = $ ....

(d) Predict the percentage of people visiting the theatre in the year 2018, according to this model. **(1)**

....

2 A 20-mile motorway extension is being planned, but there have been major delays in starting the construction.
The estimated cost, £y million, t years after the extension was first proposed can be modelled by an equation of the form $y = kb^t$, where k and b are constants to be determined.

(a) Show that the graph of $\log_{10}y$ against t will be a straight line of gradient $\log_{10}b$. **(2)**

....

(b) Write down, in terms of k, the intercept of this graph on the vertical axis. **(1)**

Intercept = ...

(c) This sketch graph shows the relationship between t and y.
Use it to work out the equation for y in terms of t. **(4)**

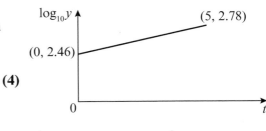

....

....

....

(d) Using this model, what was the estimated cost when the motorway extension was first proposed? **(1)**

....

(e) What would be the delay in the project if the estimated cost rose to £650 million?
Give your answer to 1 decimal place. **(2)**

....

You are the examiner!

Checking through your work is a key skill for AS maths. Have a look at pages 54 and 55 of the *Revision Guide*, then practise with these questions. There are full worked solutions on page 110.

1   The line L has equation $2y = 5 - x$

    Find the equation of the line perpendicular to L which passes through the point $(-1, 4)$

    Give your answer in the form $ax + by + c = 0$ **(5)**

....

....

....

....

2   A curve has equation $y = 3x^2 - 2x + \dfrac{4}{x}$

    Find the equation of the tangent to the curve at the point where $x = 2$

    Give your answer in the form $y = mx + c$ **(6)**

....

....

....

....

....

3   Solve the simultaneous equations

    $2x - y = 9$

    $x^2 - xy = 20$ **(7)**

....

....

....

....

....

....

4   Solve, for $0 \leqslant x \leqslant 360°$, $\cos(x + 40°) = 0.85$

    Give your answers to 1 decimal place. **(5)**

....

....

....

....

....

You are the examiner!

Checking through your work is a key skill for AS maths. Have a look at pages 54 and 55 of the *Revision Guide*, then practise with these questions. There are full worked solutions on page 110.

5 (a) Find the exact solutions of the equation $2e^{3x} + 10e^x = 9e^{2x}$ **(5)**

....

....

....

....

....

(b) Solve $4^x e^{3x+2} = 5$

Give your answer in the form $\dfrac{\ln a + b}{\ln c + d}$ where a, b, c and d are integers. **(5)**

....

....

....

....

....

6 The line with equation $y = 10 - 2x$ cuts the curve with equation $y = x^2 - 3x + 4$ at the points A and B, as shown in the diagram.

(a) Find the coordinates of A and B. **(5)**

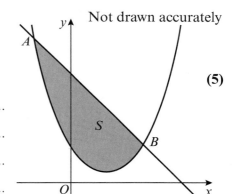

Not drawn accurately

....

....

....

....

....

(b) The shaded area, S, is bounded by the line and the curve, as shown. Find the exact area of S. **(7)**

....

....

....

....

....

....

....

....

Sampling

1 Beth is investigating how often students visit the local leisure centre. She wants a sample of 30 students from her year group of 245 students. She selects the first person from an alphabetical list by choosing a random number from 1 to 6, then selects every 8th person after that.

(a) What sampling technique is Beth using? **(1)**

....

(b) State two advantages this system of sampling has over a simple random sample. **(2)**

....

....

 2 A youth club has 450 members. Each member can play one of football, tennis, rugby and squash. The table shows the number of members who play each of these sports.

Sport	Football	Tennis	Rugby	Squash
Number of members	97	68	151	134

Bill takes a sample of 65 members, stratified by the sport they play.

Find the number of members in the sample for each of these sports. **(3)**

Sampling fraction = $\frac{..........}{450}$

> You might need to round to the nearest integer.

Number in sample playing football = $\frac{..........}{450}$ × 97 = ...

Number in sample playing:

Tennis = ...   Rugby = ...   Squash = ...

> Make sure the numbers of members in the sample add up to 65.

3 A golf club has 582 members. A stratified sample is taken, by age.
The table shows the age grouping of the members and some information about the sample.

Age (years)	16–24	25–44	45–64	65+
Number of members	96			110
Number in sample	16		34	

Complete the table. **(5)**

....

....

....

....

....

Mean

1 Over a period of weeks, 36 blackbirds were caught in a nature reserve.

They were weighed and then released.

Their masses, x grams, were such that $\sum x = 3362$

(a) Find the mean of these data. **(1)**

....

....

The next five blackbirds caught weighed

101.6 g, 104 g, 89.5 g, 94.1 g and 112.8 g.

(b) Find the mean mass of all the birds caught so far. **(2)**

> There are now 41 blackbirds.
> Calculate the new total mass.

....

....

....

Guided **2** These are the times taken, to the nearest minute, by a class of 32 students to travel to school on a particular day.

Time, t (minutes)	1–5	6–12	13–20	21–30
Frequency	6	11	7	8
Midpoint, x	3			25.5

(a) Find the midpoints of the 6–12 minutes and the 13–20 minutes groups. **(2)**

....

....

(b) Estimate the mean of the journey times for the whole class. **(2)**

$$\overline{x} = \frac{\sum fx}{\sum f} = \frac{6 \times 3 + \text{......................} + \text{......................} + 8 \times 25.5}{32}$$

$= $ ....

....

3 The table shows the distances some people travelled to work each day.

Estimate the mean distance travelled. **(4)**

Distance, d (km)	Frequency
$0 < d \leqslant 4$	9
$4 < d \leqslant 10$	17
$10 < d \leqslant 15$	33
$15 < d \leqslant 25$	24
$25 < d \leqslant 30$	11

....

....

....

....

....

Median and quartiles

Guided **1** The numbers of driving lessons taken by 23 people before they passed their test are given below.

8   17   20   32   13   23   11   33   19   33   28   35
20   28   14   27   9   28   35   26   11   34   18

(a) Write down the modal number of lessons. **(1)**

....

(b) Find the values of the lower quartile, the median and the upper quartile. **(3)**

....

....

$n = 23$, $\frac{n}{2} = 11.5 \Rightarrow$ 12th value, so median, $Q_2 = 23$

$\frac{n}{4} = 5.75 \Rightarrow$ 6th value, so $Q_1 = $ .... $\frac{3n}{4} = $ .... $\Rightarrow$ .... value, so $Q_3 = $ ....

2 Here are the ages of some people queuing for tickets at the theatre.

32   25   29   46   18   52   55   25   34   28   54   46   50
48   61   68   38   29   20   48   25   32   36   60   54   44

For these people, find the modal age, the median age and the interquartile range. **(4)**

....

....

....

....

....

....

3 The frequency table shows the scores of some golfers in the 1st round of a tournament.

Score	67	68	69	70	71	72	73	74	75	76	77
Frequency	1	2	5	9	15	7	4	0	8	0	2

Find the median and the interquartile range of these scores. **(4)**

....

....

....

....

....

Linear interpolation

1 The table gives the weights, w (kg), of 270 items of baggage checked in on a flight at Gatwick airport.

Use interpolation to estimate the median, Q_2, of these items. Give your answer correct to 1 decimal place. **(2)**

Weight, w (kg)	Number of items
$0 < w < 10$	29
$10 \leqslant w < 15$	121
$15 \leqslant w < 22$	73
$22 \leqslant w < 30$	47

$\frac{n}{2} = 135$, so the median is $(135 - 29) = 106$ values

into the $10 \leqslant w < 15$ group.

This group is 5 kg wide so each member is worth $\frac{5}{121}$ kg.

$Q_2 = 10 + 106 \times \frac{5}{121}$ kg

  $= \dots\dots\dots\dots$ kg

2 The table shows the speeds, v (mph), of 90 vehicles travelling along a country road.

(a) Use interpolation to estimate the median, Q_2, the lower quartile, Q_1, and the upper quartile, Q_3, of these items.
Give your answers correct to 1 decimal place. **(4)**

Speed, v (mph)	Number of vehicles
$10 \leqslant v < 20$	12
$20 \leqslant v < 30$	16
$30 \leqslant v < 45$	36
$45 \leqslant v < 60$	18
$60 \leqslant v < 70$	8

....

....

....

....

....

> Start by working out $\frac{n}{4}, \frac{n}{2}$ and $\frac{3n}{4}$ to locate the positions of Q_1, Q_2 and Q_3 then follow the same procedure as in Question 1.

(b) Local residents claim that at least 20% of vehicles are breaking the 50 mph speed limit.

Investigate their claim. **(3)**

> Work out the 80th percentile.

....

....

3 The table shows the lengths of caterpillars, measured to the nearest millimetre.

Use interpolation to estimate the median, Q_2, the lower quartile, Q_1, and the upper quartile, Q_3, of these items. Give your answers correct to 1 decimal place. **(4)**

Length (mm)	Frequency
1–10	16
11–25	33
26–45	38
46–65	27
66–75	10

....

....

....

> **Problem solving** Be aware of the upper and lower class boundaries, e.g. 11–25 really means lengths from 10.5 to 25.5 mm.

....

....

....

Standard deviation 1

Guided 1 The table shows the marks obtained (out of 80) by students in a maths exam.

Given that $\sum x^2 = 195\,600$, calculate estimates for the mean and the standard deviation for the data. **(6)**

Mark	Frequency (f)	Midpoint (x)	$f \times x$
$0 < x \leqslant 10$	16	5	80
$10 < x \leqslant 30$	32	20	
$30 < x \leqslant 50$	38		
$50 < x \leqslant 60$	24		
$60 < x \leqslant 80$	10		

....

....

....

....

2 The ages, x years, of 34 people in a restaurant can be summarised as follows:

$$\sum x = 1262 \text{ and } \sum x^2 = 54\,431$$

Calculate the mean and the standard deviation of these ages. **(3)**

....

....

....

....

3 The heights, h cm, of 45 plants are recorded correct to the nearest centimetre. The summary data is:

$$\sum h = 1568 \text{ and } \sum h^2 = 60\,668$$

Calculate estimates of the mean and the standard deviation of their heights. **(3)**

....

....

....

....

4 Here is a record of the numbers of letters received, in a week, by households in a street.

13   20   31   15   18   29   20   31   18

26   21   32   26   19   24   34   15   24

Calculate the mean and the standard deviation of the data. **(3)**

....

....

....

....

Standard deviation 2

> **Guided**

1 The table shows the times taken by 160 people to travel to work one morning.

Estimate the standard deviation of the data.

(5)

Time, t (minutes)	Number of people	Midpoint
$0 \leqslant t < 10$	12	5
$10 \leqslant t < 15$	27	12.5
$15 \leqslant t < 30$	85	22.5
$30 \leqslant t < 50$	36	40

$$\sum f = 160$$

$$\sum fx = 12 \times 5 + 27 \times 12.5 + 85 \times 22.5 + 36 \times 40$$

$$= 3750$$

$$\sum fx^2 = 12 \times 5^2 + 27 \times 12.5^2 + \text{.................} + \text{.................}$$

$$= \text{.................}$$

$$\text{Variance} = \frac{\text{.................}}{160} - \left(\frac{3750}{160}\right)^2 = \text{.................}$$

> Start by finding the midpoint of each group – these will be the x values. Work out $\sum fx$ and $\sum fx^2$, then use the formula for the variance. Don't forget to square root to find the standard deviation.

....

....

2 The profits of 92 businesses are given in the table.

Estimate the standard deviation of the data. **(5)**

Profit, p (£ million)	Number of businesses
$1.0 \leqslant p < 2.0$	19
$2.0 \leqslant p < 2.8$	34
$2.8 \leqslant p < 3.6$	26
$3.6 \leqslant p < 5.0$	13

....

....

....

....

....

....

3 The table shows the lengths of some earthworms, measured to the nearest millimetre.

(a) Find the midpoints of the 30–46 and 66–75 groups. **(2)**

Length (mm)	Frequency	Midpoint
11–29	16	20
30–46	36	
47–65	40	56
66–75	24	
76–100	10	88
101–120	14	110.5

....

....

(b) Estimate the standard deviation of the lengths of these earthworms. **(3)**

[You may use $\sum fx^2 = 551\,493.5$]

....

....

....

....

Coding

> **Guided**

1 The table shows the yields of potatoes, w kg, from some allotments.

Yield, w (kg)	Frequency (f)	Midpoint (w)	$u(w - 80)$	$f \times u$	u^2	$f \times u^2$
$65 \leqslant w < 75$	21	70	-10	-210	100	2100
$75 \leqslant w < 85$	18	80	0			
$85 \leqslant w < 105$	11					
$105 \leqslant w < 125$	7					

Use the coding $u = w - 80$ to work out estimates
of the mean and the standard deviation of the data.
Give your answers to 3 significant figures. **(6)**

> Coding simplifies the calculations in the table significantly.

Mean for $u = \dfrac{\sum fu}{n} = \dfrac{\text{.........}}{57} = \text{.........}$, so mean for $w = \text{............} + 80 = \text{............}$ kg (3 s.f.)

Variance for $u = \dfrac{\sum fu^2}{n} - \left[\dfrac{\sum fu}{n}\right]^2 = \dfrac{\text{.........}}{57} - (\text{............})^2 = \text{............}$

> The mean for w needs adjusting but the SD does not.

Standard deviation for $u = \; = \sqrt{\text{............}} = \text{............}$, so standard

deviation for $w = \text{............}$ kg (3 s.f.)

2 The time taken, t minutes, for a task is coded using $y = \dfrac{t - 12.5}{8}$

The mean of the coded data is $\bar{y} = 1.6$
The standard deviation of the coded data is $\sigma_y = 1.12$
Find the mean and the standard deviation of the original data. **(2)**

....

....

3 The scores, x, in a test for 50 people are shown in the table.

Score, x	Frequency
$100 < x \leqslant 106$	6
$106 < x \leqslant 114$	12
$114 < x \leqslant 126$	23
$126 < x \leqslant 140$	9

(a) Find estimates of the mean and the standard deviation of the scores.
You may use the fact that $\sum x^2 = 699\,255$ **(4)**

....

....

(b) It was discovered that there had been an error in the marking, and all the scores were
adjusted by subtracting 3 marks and then increasing them by 5%.
Find estimates of the mean and the standard deviation of the adjusted marks. **(2)**

....

....

Box plots and outliers

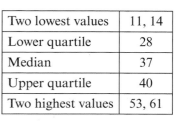

Guided 1 Carla recorded the ages of some people at a concert.
This table summarises her data.

Two lowest values	11, 14
Lower quartile	28
Median	37
Upper quartile	40
Two highest values	53, 61

An outlier is a value that is greater than Q_3 plus 1.25 times the interquartile range or less than Q_1 minus 1.25 times the interquartile range.

Draw a box plot to represent the data, indicating clearly any outliers. **(5)**

IQR = 40 − 28 = 12

1.25 × IQR = 1.25 × 12 = ...

Q_3 + ... = ...

....

....

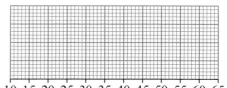

10 15 20 25 30 35 40 45 50 55 60 65

2 The box plot shows a summary of the marks gained by students in a test.
(a) (i) Write down the mark that 75% of the students scored more than.
(ii) State the name given to this mark. **(2)**

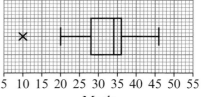

5 10 15 20 25 30 35 40 45 50 55
Mark

....

....

An outlier is a value greater than Q_3 plus 1.5 times the interquartile range or less than Q_1 minus 1.5 times the interquartile range.

(b) Show working to explain why 10 is an outlier. **(2)**

....

....

3 A town centre car park was monitored every half hour, over an 11-hour period, to record how many cars were parked.
These are the results:

    26 18 27 36 27 43   9 30 48 36 29
    15 28   7 26 19 53 26 31 37 28 31

An outlier is a value that is greater than Q_3 plus 1.5 times the interquartile range or less than Q_1 minus 1.5 times the interquartile range.

Draw a box plot to represent the data, indicating clearly any outliers. **(7)**

....

....

....

....

....

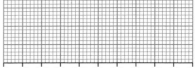

5 10 15 20 25 30 35 40 45 50 55

....

....

Cumulative frequency diagrams

> **Guided** 1 The table shows the lengths of some insects in a zoo, measured to the nearest millimetre.

Length, l (mm)	Number of insects	Cumulative frequency
$0 < l \leq 5$	65	65
$5 < l \leq 10$	50	115
$10 < l \leq 20$	60	
$20 < l \leq 30$	25	
$30 < l \leq 40$	15	
$40 < l \leq 50$	10	

(a) Draw a cumulative frequency diagram to represent the data. **(3)**

(b) Use your cumulative frequency diagram to estimate the 20th to 80th interpercentile range. **(3)**

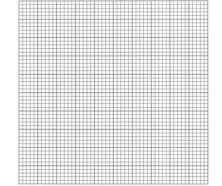

For the 20th percentile, read across from $\frac{20n}{100}$ on the vertical axis then down to the horizontal axis.

20th percentile $= \frac{20}{100} \times 225 = $ ....th value

80th percentile $= \frac{80}{100} \times 225 = $ ....th value

Interpercentile range $= $ .... $-$ .... $= $ .... mm

2 Katie did a survey of the amounts of money spent by customers in a supermarket one morning. The table shows her results.

Amount spent, x (£)	$0 < x \leq 10$	$10 < x \leq 20$	$20 < x \leq 40$	$40 < x \leq 60$	$60 < x \leq 80$	$80 < x \leq 100$
Number of customers	12	42	70	28	20	8

(a) Draw a cumulative frequency diagram to represent the data. **(3)**

(b) Use your cumulative frequency diagram to find the median and the interquartile range of the amounts spent. **(3)**

....

....

....

....

(c) Estimate how many people spent more than £75. **(2)**

....

(d) Estimate the 10th to 90th interpercentile range. **(2)**

....

Histograms

Guided 1 The histogram shows information about how much time cars spent in a car park.

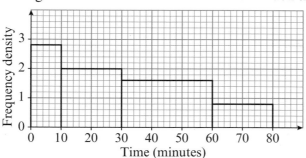

Frequency density × class width = frequency

Complete the table. **(2)**

Frequency for 0 < t ≤ 10 class = 2.8 × 10 = 28

Frequency for 10 < t ≤ 30 class = 2 × .... = ...

....

....

Time, t (minutes)	Number of cars
0 < t ≤ 10	28
10 < t ≤ 30	
30 < t ≤ 60	
60 < t ≤ 80	16

2 The speeds of cars along a stretch of road were recorded.

The histogram and the frequency table show the same information.

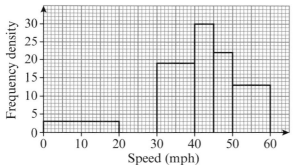

Speed, v (mph)	Number of cars
0 < v ≤ 20	60
20 < v ≤ 30	110
30 < v ≤ 40	190
40 < v ≤ 45	150
45 < v ≤ 50	
50 < v ≤ 60	130

(a) Complete the histogram and fill in the missing number in the frequency table. **(2)**

....

(b) Estimate how many cars were travelling at between 25 mph and 43 mph. **(3)**

....

....

....

3 Poppy recorded the heights of 80 plant seedlings, to the nearest mm. This table shows her results.

Problem solving The 6–7 bar is plotted from 5.5 to 7.5 so it has width 2.

Height (mm)	6–7	8–9	10–13	14–19
Frequency	8	32	24	18

A histogram was drawn and the bar representing the 8–9 class was 1 cm wide and 4 cm high. Find the width and the height of the bar representing the 10–13 class. **(3)**

....

....

....

Comparing distributions

> **Guided**

1 The box plots show the marks scored in an exam by the boys and the girls in a class.

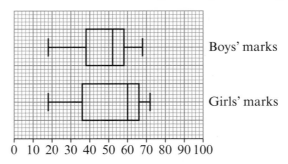

Boys' marks

Girls' marks

0 10 20 30 40 50 60 70 80 90 100

Compare and contrast the two sets of results. **(4)**

The median for the boys' marks (52) is less than the median for the girls' marks (60),

so the boys did less well overall.

The IQR for the boys was .... compared with .... for the girls.

....

....

> **Problem solving** You need to compare data sets using a measure of location and a measure of spread

2 Two classes, PX and HY, sat a maths exam that was marked out of 50.
The table shows the breakdown of the marks for class PX.

Mark	Number of students
$10 < x \leqslant 20$	2
$20 < x \leqslant 30$	6
$30 < x \leqslant 40$	8
$40 < x \leqslant 50$	14

(a) Use the summary statistic $\sum x^2 = 42\,410$ to calculate estimates for the mean and the standard deviation for class PX. **(4)**

....

....

....

....

(b) The mean and standard deviation for class HY are:

   Mean = 32.8   Standard deviation = 7.45

The median for class PX is 39. The median for class HY is 31.
Compare and contrast the results of the two classes. **(3)**

....

....

....

....

Correlation and cleaning data

Guided **1** A scientist is testing a model that proposes that an increase in weight is usually accompanied by an increase in height in teenage boys. This table shows the weights and the heights of some teenage boys.

	A	B	C	D	E	F	G	H	I	J	K	L
Weight, w (kg)	72	80	58	71	68	72	67	55	72	73	77	70
Height, h (cm)	175	182	166	173	172	180	169	173	176	182	178	174

The following statistics were calculated for the data on weight:

$Q_1 = 67.5$ $Q_2 = 71.5$ $Q_3 = 72.5$

An outlier is defined as a value that is more than $3 \times$ IQR above or below the median.

(a) Show that $x = 55$ is an outlier. **(1)**

IQR = 72.5 − 67.5 = 5, 3 × IQR = 15, 71.5 − 15 = ..., which is ....

(b) It was decided to remove boy H from the data. Comment on the validity of this decision. **(2)**

....

....

(c) Draw a scatter diagram for the remaining 11 results. **(3)**

(d) Describe the correlation shown on your scatter diagram and interpret this in the context of the model. **(2)**

....

....

....

2 Simon is conducting an experiment on memory.
He randomly selects ten people and gives them 20 minutes to try to remember 30 words.
Then, after a gap of 10 minutes, he asks them to recall as many words as possible.
The table shows the age of each person, x years and the number of words remembered, y.

	A	B	C	D	E	F	G	H	I	J
Age, x (years)	19	32	16	70	48	34	30	39	29	36
Number of words, y	15	15	19	20	17	18	12	13	23	14

(a) Find Q_1, Q_2 and Q_3 for the ages of the people. **(3)**

....

An outlier is defined as a value that is more than $3 \times$ IQR above or below the median.

(b) Show that $x = 70$ is an outlier. **(1)**

....

(c) Simon decides to retain person D in his results.
Comment on his decision. **(2)**

....

....

Regression

Guided **1** Measurements of annual average CO_2 levels have been recorded at Mauna Loa in Hawaii.

The scatter diagram shows the CO_2 level, y, in parts per million and the number of years, x, since 1991.

The equation of the regression line of y on x for the data is

$$y = 351.64 + 2.11x$$

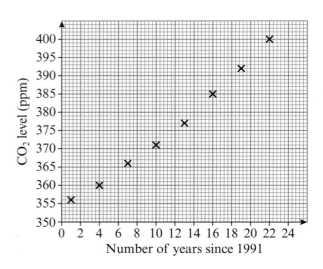

(a) Give an interpretation of the gradient of the regression line. **(1)**

The gradient is 2.11, so every year the

average CO_2 level ....

....

(b) Comment on the validity of a linear regression model for the data. **(2)**

There is .... correlation so a linear model ....

2 The scatter diagram shows the average daily temperature, x°C, and a household's daily energy consumption, y kWh, on 8 winter days.

The equation of the regression line of y on x for the data is

$$y = 25.7 - 2.25x$$

(a) Give an interpretation of the gradient of the regression line. **(1)**

....

....

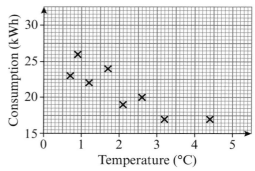

(b) Give an interpretation of the y-intercept of the regression line. **(1)**

....

(c) Comment on the validity of a linear regression model for the data. **(2)**

....

....

....

Using regression lines

1   Explain what is meant by

(a) interpolation **(1)**

....

(b) extrapolation. **(2)**

....

2   Look at the information and scatter diagram from Question 1 on the previous page.

The equation of the regression line of y on x is $y = 351.64 + 2.11x$, where x is the number of years since 1991 and y is the average level of CO_2 in parts per million.

(a) Comment on the reliability of using this regression equation to estimate the average level of CO_2 in

(i) 2005

(ii) 2016. **(2)**

....

....

....

(b) Laura uses the above regression model to predict the year in which CO_2 levels reached 375 parts per million. Give a reason why this regression model would not be suitable for this prediction. **(1)**

....

3   Look at the information and scatter diagram from Question 2 on the previous page.

The equation of the regression line of y on x is $y = 25.7 - 2.25x$, where x is the temperature in °C and y is the daily energy consumption in kWh.

(a) Comment on the reliability of using this regression equation to estimate

(i) the daily energy consumption when the average temperature is 4 °C

(ii) the average temperature on a day when the household used 20 kWh of energy. **(2)**

....

....

....

(b) Tom states that the regression model predicts that each additional °C of temperature reduces energy usage by 2.25 kWh. He predicts that if the weather is warmer than 12 °C, the household will use no energy.

Give two reasons why Tom's prediction is unlikely to be accurate. **(2)**

....

....

Drawing Venn diagrams

Guided   **1**   80 children were asked whether they had a cat, a dog or a rabbit as a pet.

     31 of them had a cat
     35 of them had a dog
     18 of them had a rabbit
     11 of them had a cat and a dog
     7 of them had a cat and a rabbit
     5 of them had a dog and a rabbit
     2 of them had all three pets

(a) Draw a Venn diagram to represent this information.   **(5)**

The 11 children who had a cat and a dog include the 2 children who had all three pets.

So 11 − 2 = 9 children had a cat and a dog but not a rabbit. This is C and D but not R.

....

....

....

....

....

....

(b) How many of the 80 children did not have a cat or a dog?   **(1)**

....

2   160 people were asked which of the countries France, Italy and Germany they had visited.

     78 of them had been to France
     43 of them had been to Italy
     69 of them had been to Germany
     21 of them had been to France and Italy
     31 of them had been to France and Germany
     20 of them had been to Italy and Germany
     14 of them had been to all three countries

> Draw a rectangle to denote the whole sample space and draw three closed, intersecting circles for the three events, labelled F, I and G, inside the rectangle.

(a) Draw a Venn diagram to represent this information.   **(5)**

....

....

....

....

....

....

....

(b) How many of the 160 people had been to exactly two of the three countries?   **(1)**

....

Using Venn diagrams

Guided

1 The Venn diagram shows the numbers of students who take maths, English and history.

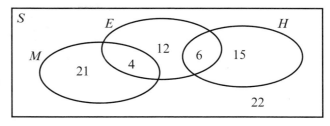

One of these students is selected at random.

(a) Show that the probability that the student takes only one of the subjects is $\frac{3}{5}$

      (2)

The total number of students = 21 + 4 + 12 + 6 + 15 + 22 = 80

The number taking only one subject = 21 + 12 + ... = ...

So the probability is ....

(b) Find the probability that the student takes maths or English, or both.   **(2)**

....

2 For the events *A* (art) and *B* (biology), 23% of the students take both *A* and *B*, 54% of the students take *B* and 17% of the students take neither *A* nor *B*.

(a) Draw a Venn diagram to illustrate the complete sample space for events *A* and *B*.   **(4)**

> Write probabilities as percentages on the Venn diagram. The total in the whole sample space must be 100%.

(b) What percentage of the students take art?   **(1)**

....

3 A survey showed that 68% of the people in a town shopped at Warners supermarket and 46% shopped at Johnsons supermarket. 17% of the people in the town did not shop at either of these supermarkets.

(a) Draw a Venn diagram to represent this information.   **(4)**

A person from the town is chosen at random.

(b) Write down the probability that this person shops at either Warners or Johnsons, but not both.   **(2)**

....

Independent events

1   Given that $P(Q) = q$ and $P(R) = r$, express $P(Q \text{ or } R)$ in terms of q and r when

   (a) Q and R are mutually exclusive   **(1)**

   ....

   (b) Q and R are independent.   **(1)**

   ....

Guided   2   The Venn diagram shows the numbers of people who chose a chocolate biscuit (C), a wafer biscuit (W) or a ginger biscuit (G) from a box of biscuits.

   Determine whether choosing a chocolate biscuit and choosing a ginger biscuit are statistically independent.   **(3)**

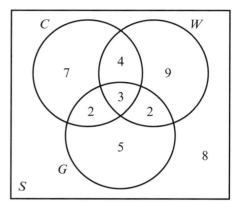

   Total number of people

   $$= 7 + 4 + 9 + 2 + 3 + 2 + 5 + 8 = \text{............}$$

   $$P(C) = \frac{7 + 4 + 2 + 3}{\text{.........}} = \frac{16}{\text{.........}}$$

   $$P(G) = \frac{5 + 2 + \text{.........} + \text{.........}}{\text{.........}} =$$

   Next, work out $P(C \text{ and } G)$ and compare it to $P(C) \times P(G)$.

   ....

   ....

3   Two events A and B are independent.

   $$P(B \text{ and not } A) = \frac{3}{25} \qquad P(\text{neither } A \text{ nor } B) = \frac{1}{5}$$

   Draw a Venn diagram and mark on it the probabilities that are given.

   (a) Find $P(A)$ **(3)**

   ....

   (b) Find $P(A \text{ and } B)$ **(4)**

    Problem solving Let $P(A \text{ and } B) = x$ Use the fact that A and B are independent and set up an equation to find x.

   ....

   ....

   ....

   ....

   ....

Tree diagrams

> **Guided**

1 Marcus either gets up immediately when his alarm goes off or sleeps for a little while longer. The probability that he gets up immediately is 0.3

If he gets up immediately, the probability that he eats breakfast is 0.85 but if he sleeps for a little while longer, the probability that he eats breakfast is 0.45

(a) Draw a tree diagram to represent this information. **(2)**

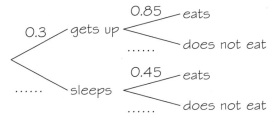

(b) Find the probability that Marcus does not eat breakfast. **(3)**

Remember to include both cases,
P(gets up and does not eat) + P(sleeps and does not eat).

....

....

(c) Find the probability that Marcus does not eat breakfast on 2 days out of 3. **(3)**

Problem solving This can be done in more than one way, e.g. day 1: does not eat; day 2: eats; day 3: does not eat.

....

....

....

2 When Keisha goes to a restaurant she always eats pizza or risotto for her main course and always eats apple pie or lemon tart for dessert.

The probability that she eats pizza is $\frac{3}{8}$

If she eats pizza, the probability that she eats apple pie is $\frac{4}{5}$

If she eats risotto, the probability that she eats lemon tart is $\frac{2}{3}$

(a) Draw a tree diagram to represent this information. **(2)**

(b) Find the probability that Keisha eats either risotto or lemon tart, but not both. **(3)**

....

....

(c) Find the probability that Keisha eats risotto followed by lemon tart on two successive visits to the restaurant. **(3)**

....

....

....

Random variables

> **Guided**

1 The discrete random variable X can only take the values 1, 2, 3 and 4

X has probability function

$$P(X = x) = \begin{cases} kx^2, & x = 1, 2, 3 \\ 3kx, & x = 4 \end{cases}$$

where k is a constant.

(a) Find the value of k and construct a table giving the probability distribution of X. **(3)**

$P(X = 1) = k \times 1^2 = k$, $P(X = 2) = k \times 2^2 = 4k$, $P(X = 3) = $ ...., $P(X = 4) = $ ....

$k + 4k + $ .... $+ $ .... $= 1$, giving $k = $ ....

x	1	2	3	4
$P(X = x)$				

(b) Find $P(X < 3)$. **(2)**

....

2 The discrete random variable Y can only take the values 1, 2, 3, 4 and 5

Y has probability function $P(Y = y) = k(6y - y^2)$ for $y = 1, 2, 3, 4, 5$, where k is a constant.

(a) Construct a table giving the probability distribution of Y. **(3)**

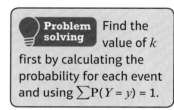

Problem solving Find the value of k first by calculating the probability for each event and using $\sum P(Y = y) = 1$.

(b) Find $P(Y \geqslant 3)$. **(2)**

....

3 The discrete random variable W has the probability distribution given by

w	-4	-1	0	1	3	6
$P(W = w)$	0.15	$2a$	a	0.05	0.1	$0.5a$

where a is a constant.

(a) Find the value of a. **(2)**

....

....

....

(b) Find $P(2W + 5 \geqslant 4)$. **(2)**

....

....

....

....

The binomial distribution

> **Guided**

1 Research shows that 5% of people are allergic to a particular brand of hand cream.
A group of 40 people, randomly chosen, agree to test the product.

(a) Justify the use of the binomial distribution to model the number of people in the group who are allergic. **(2)**

....

(b) Find the probability that exactly two of the people are allergic to the hand cream. **(2)**

$$P(X = 2) = \binom{40}{2} \times (0.05)^2 \times (\text{............})^{38} = \text{............}$$

(c) Find the probability that no more than two of the people are allergic to the hand cream. **(2)**

| This is P(0) + P(1) + P(2) or, $P(X \le 2)$, using the binomial cumulative distribution. |

....

....

2 In one category of a quiz there are 8 questions.
For each question there is a choice of three possible answers, only one of which is correct.
Jack has no knowledge of this topic so decides to guess every answer.

(a) Find the probability that he gets exactly five questions correct. **(2)**

....

(b) Find the probability that he gets at least two correct answers. **(2)**

....

....

3 Ellie has a bag containing 20 liquorice sweets and 20 toffees. She eats 10 sweets at random, and records the number of toffees, T, that she eats. Ellie decided to model T as B(10, 0.5). Explain why this model is not suitable. **(1)**

....

....

4 The probability that a plant produces pink flowers is 0.35
A garden centre sells these plants in trays of 12 plants of mixed colours.
A tray is selected at random.
Find the probability that, in this tray, the number of plants that will produce pink flowers is:

(a) exactly 4 **(2)**

....

(b) more than 5 **(2)**

....

(c) between 3 and 6 (inclusive). **(3)**

....

....

Hypothesis testing

> **Guided**

1 When playing a game involving dice, Elaine noticed that a score of 1 seemed to occur more than might be expected.

She tested her theory that the dice was biased towards the number 1 by throwing it 30 times and recording the scores. Her results are shows in the table.

Score	1	2	3	4	5	6
Frequency	8	4	5	3	6	4

Test, at the 10% significance level, whether there is sufficient evidence that the dice is biased towards the number 1. **(6)**

H_0: $P(1) = \frac{1}{6}$ (unbiased) H_1: $P(1) > \frac{1}{6}$ (biased)

Assume H_0, so that $X \sim B(30, \frac{1}{6})$ where X is the number of 1s

$P(X \leqslant 7) = $ .... $P(X \geqslant 8) = 1 - $ .... $ = $ ....

Since .... 0.10 , there is .... evidence to reject H_0

So the conclusion is that ....

2 In a local football team, the striker who takes the penalties thinks he has a fairly unimpressive 55% chance of scoring from a penalty.
His coach thinks he is underestimating his chances.
The striker takes 18 penalties and scores 14 times.
Test at the 5% significance level whether he has underestimated his chances of scoring.
State your hypotheses clearly. **(6)**

....

....

....

....

....

3 In the 2016 UK referendum, 51.9% of those voting voted for the UK to leave the EU.
In a sample of 50 Scottish voters, 19 said they voted to leave.
Test at the 5% significance level whether this result is different from the UK average.
State your hypotheses clearly. **(6)**

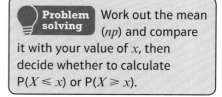

Problem solving Work out the mean (np) and compare it with your value of x, then decide whether to calculate $P(X \leqslant x)$ or $P(X \geqslant x)$.

....

....

....

....

....

....

....

Critical regions

Guided **1** Peppered moths can be light or dark. In a village 20% of the moths are dark.
Atmospheric pollution can be identified by an increase in the proportion of dark moths.
A scientist wants to investigate whether pollution levels are changing so she catches a sample of 30 moths and counts how many of them are dark.
Find the critical values at the 10% significance level that would indicate that pollution levels are changing. **(3)**

Model this by $X \sim B(30, 0.2)$ $H_0: p = 0.2$ $H_1: p$ .... (two-tailed test)

$P(X \leqslant 2) =$ .... $P(X \leqslant$ .... $) =$ ....

$P(X \geqslant$ .... $) =$ .... $P(X \geqslant$ .... $) =$ ....

> You are finding probabilities as close as possible to 0.05 but < 0.05.

The critical region is .... and ....

So catching fewer than .... or more than .... dark moths would indicate that

pollution levels are changing.

2 In the UK 22% of the people have brown eyes.
It is suspected that in the South-West of England, this figure is higher.
To test this theory, a sample of 40 people living in the South-West were randomly selected.

(a) Using a 5% significance level, find the critical region for this test, clearly stating your hypotheses. **(3)**

....

....

....

(b) State the actual significance level of this test. **(1)**

....

(c) The number of people found to have brown eyes in the sample was 12.
Comment on this observation in the light of your critical region. **(2)**

....

....

3 A random variable, X, is modelled as $X \sim B(36, p)$
A single observation of X is taken and used to test $H_0: p = 0.73$ against $H_1: p \neq 0.73$

(a) Using a 5% significance level, find the critical region for this test. **(2)**

....

....

(b) State the actual significance level. **(1)**

....

(c) The observed value of X is 19.
Comment on this observation in the light of your critical region. **(2)**

....

....

You are the examiner!

Checking through your work is a key skill for AS maths. Have a look at pages 78 and 79 of the *Revision Guide*, then practise with these questions. There are full worked solutions on page 114.

1   An inspector is checking a company's vehicles.

There are 3 large-load vehicles, 135 light vans and 24 company cars.

The inspector decides to sample 15% of the vehicles. Each type of vehicle should be included in the sample.

(a) What is this sampling procedure called?   **(1)**

....

(b) How many of each type of vehicle should be inspected?   **(3)**

....

....

2   The numbers of goals scored, x, and points gained, y, by 10 netball teams are shown in the table.

Team	A	B	C	D	E	F	G	H	I	J
Goals, x	37	51	51	46	48	30	56	60	45	50
Points, y	15	21	14	18	17	10	19	14	11	16

(a) Find the values of the median and the interquartile range for the goals scored.   **(3)**

....

....

An outlier is defined as a value that is more than $3 \times IQR$ above the median or below the median.

(b) Show that $x = 30$ is an outlier.   **(1)**

....

(c) Explain why the data for team F should be retained.   **(2)**

....

....

(d) Draw a scatter diagram for all 10 data items.   **(3)**

(e) Describe and interpret the correlation shown on your scatter diagram.   **(2)**

....

....

....

....

....

You are the examiner!

Checking through your work is a key skill for AS maths. Have a look at pages 78 and 79 of the *Revision Guide*, then practise with these questions. There are full worked solutions on page 114.

3 Electric cable is sold on reels which are supposed to hold 100 m of cable.

For quality control purposes the length is checked by measuring randomly chosen reels.

The lengths are recorded as differences, in centimetres, from 100 m, so, for example, a sample of 99.87 m is recorded as -13

For a sample of $n = 20$ reels, the data are summarised as follows:

$$\sum x = -88 \text{ and } \sum x^2 = 4292$$

(a) Calculate the mean and standard deviation of the values of x. **(3)**

....

....

(b) Hence find the mean and the standard deviation, in metres, of the lengths of cable on the 20 reels. **(2)**

....

....

Someone notices that one of the x values is -38, and thinks it might be an error, so it is discarded.

(c) Find the new mean and the standard deviation, in metres, of the lengths of cable on the other 19 reels. **(3)**

....

....

....

....

4 In a tea shop, 65% of the customers take tea with milk, 15% take tea with lemon and the rest take tea with neither milk nor lemon.

Of those taking tea with milk, $\frac{2}{5}$ take sugar.

Of those taking tea with lemon, $\frac{1}{4}$ take sugar.

Of those taking tea with neither milk nor lemon, $\frac{3}{8}$ take sugar.

(a) Represent this information on a fully labelled tree diagram. **(3)**

(b) Find the probability that a customer does not take sugar. **(4)**

....

....

Modelling in mechanics

1   A block of wood A rests on a smooth table and is attached to one end of a light inextensible string. The string passes over a smooth pulley P fixed at the edge of the table. The other end of the string is attached to a ball B which hangs freely below the pulley.

The system is released from rest with the string taut. In the resulting motion A and B are modelled as particles. State how you can use in your calculations that

(a) the plane is smooth   **(1)**   [Think about the friction.]

....

(b) the string is light   **(1)**   [Think about the weight.]

....

(c) the string is inextensible   **(1)**   [Think about the acceleration.]

....

(d) the pulley is smooth   **(1)**

....

(e) A and B are modelled as particles.   **(1)**

....

2   A mass of 1 kg is attached to a fixed point by a string.
    It hangs vertically, in equilibrium.   [Consider the string, the mass
    The mass is pulled to one side and released.   and the motion of the mass.]

Make a list of the assumptions you might make to create a simple model for this situation.   **(3)**

....

....

....

3   A football is kicked and its path can be modelled by the equation $h = 0.8x - 0.009x^2$ where h m is the height of the ball above the ground and x m is the horizontal distance travelled.

(a) Find the height of the ball when it has travelled 20 m horizontally.   **(2)**

....

....

(b) How far will the ball travel before it hits the ground? Give your answer to 3 s.f.   **(2)**

....

....

(c) What is the greatest height reached by the ball? Give your answer to 3 s.f.   **(2)**

....

....

(d) What assumptions have been made in calculations using this model for the path of the
     football?   **(2)**

....

Motion graphs

Guided 1 A car is moving along a straight horizontal road. The speed of the car as it passes the point A is $30\,\mathrm{m\,s^{-1}}$ and the car maintains this speed for $40\,\mathrm{s}$. The car then decelerates uniformly to a speed of $20\,\mathrm{m\,s^{-1}}$. The speed of $20\,\mathrm{m\,s^{-1}}$ is then maintained until the car passes the point B. The time taken to travel from A to B is $100\,\mathrm{s}$ and $AB = 2500\,\mathrm{m}$.

(a) Sketch a velocity–time graph to show the motion of the car from A to B. **(2)**

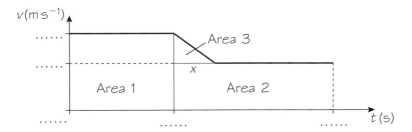

> Divide the area under the graph into separate sections to calculate the total area.

(b) Calculate the deceleration of the car as it decelerates from $30\,\mathrm{m\,s^{-1}}$ to $20\,\mathrm{m\,s^{-1}}$. **(7)**

Area = Area 1 + Area 2 + Area 3

$= (30 \times 40) + (20 \times \,\underline{\hspace{1cm}}\,) + (\frac{1}{2} \times \,\underline{\hspace{1cm}}\, \times x) = 2500$

.... $x =$ ....

Deceleration $= \dfrac{\overline{\hspace{1cm}}}{\underline{\hspace{1cm}}} =$ .... $\mathrm{m\,s^{-2}}$

> Distance travelled = area under graph

> Find the gradient of the graph to work out the deceleration.

2 A train is travelling at $12\,\mathrm{m\,s^{-1}}$ on a straight horizontal track. The driver sees a red signal $150\,\mathrm{m}$ ahead and immediately applies the brakes. The train immediately decelerates with constant deceleration for $10\,\mathrm{s}$, reducing its speed to $4\,\mathrm{m\,s^{-1}}$. The driver then releases the brakes and allows the train to travel at a constant speed of $4\,\mathrm{m\,s^{-1}}$ for a further $10\,\mathrm{s}$. He then applies the brakes again and the train slows down with constant deceleration, coming to rest as it reaches the signal.

(a) Sketch a velocity–time graph to show the motion of the train. **(3)**

(b) Find the distance travelled by the train from the moment when the brakes are first applied to the moment when its speed first reaches $4\,\mathrm{m\,s^{-1}}$. **(2)**

....

....

....

(c) Find the total time from the moment when the brakes are first applied to the moment when the train comes to rest. **(5)**

....

....

....

....

Constant acceleration 1

Guided   **1**   A car moves with constant acceleration along a straight horizontal road. The car passes the point A with speed $5 \, m \, s^{-1}$ and 4 s later it passes the point B, with a speed of $20 \, m \, s^{-1}$.

(a) Find the acceleration of the car.   **(2)**

$s = ? \qquad u = 5 \qquad v = 20 \qquad a = ? \qquad t = 4$

$v = u + at$

.... = ... $+ \, a \times 4$

....

....

> Constant acceleration means using the *suvat* formulae. Write down the five letters and all the values you know.

> Use $v = u + at$ and solve to find a.

(b) Find the distance AB.   **(2)**

$s = ? \qquad u = 5 \qquad v = 20 \qquad a = \text{.........} \qquad t = 4$

$s = \dfrac{1}{2}(\text{.....................})\text{.........} = \text{.................................}$ m

> Use $s = \frac{1}{2}(u + v)t$.

2   A particle P is moving with constant acceleration along a straight horizontal line ABC where $AC = 25 \, m$. Initially P is at A and is moving with speed $6 \, m \, s^{-1}$ in the direction AB. After 2.5 s, P is at B with speed $10.5 \, m \, s^{-1}$.

> When the question involves **three points** draw a sketch to help you.

(a) Find the acceleration of the particle.   **(2)**

....

....

....

....

(b) Find the distance BC.   **(3)**

....

....

....

3   The driver of a train begins the approach to a station by applying the brakes when the speed is $40 \, m \, s^{-1}$. The train takes 30 s to come to rest at the station.

> When the train comes to rest, $v = 0$.

(a) Find the deceleration of the train.   **(2)**

....

....

....

(b) Find the distance between the train and the station when the driver applied the brakes.   **(2)**

....

....

....

Constant acceleration 2

Guided   **1**   Three posts P, Q and R are fixed in that order at the side of a straight horizontal road. The distance from P to Q is 45 m and the distance from Q to R is 120 m. A car is moving along the road with constant acceleration a m s^{-2}. The speed of the car, as it passes P, is u m s^{-1}. The car passes Q 2 s after passing P, and the car passes R 4 s after passing Q.

Find the value of u and the value of a.   **(7)**

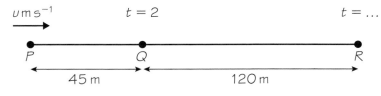

> When the question involves **three points**, draw a sketch to help you.

PQ: $s = 45$ $u = u$ $\cancel{v = ?}$ $a = a$ $t = 2$

$45 = u \times \text{.........} + \frac{1}{2}a \times \text{.........}^2$ ①

> Use $s = ut + \frac{1}{2}at^2$ for PQ and PR and solve simultaneously.

PR: $s = \text{.........}$ $u = u$ $\cancel{v = ?}$ $a = a$ $t = \text{.........}$

$\text{.........} = u \times \text{.........} + \frac{1}{2}a \times \text{.........}^2$ ②

....

....

....

....

2   Two cars A and B are moving in the same direction along a straight horizontal road. At time $t = 0$, they are side by side, passing a point O on the road. Car A travels at a constant speed of 40 m s^{-1}. Car B passes O with a speed of 25 m s^{-1}, and has constant acceleration of 5 m s^{-2}. Find

(a)   the speed of B when it has travelled 80 m from O **(2)**

> Use $v^2 = u^2 + 2as$ for B.

....

....

....

(b)   the distance from O of A when B is 80 m from O **(4)**

....

> Find the time taken for B to travel 80 m from O.

....

> For constant speed, $a = 0$ so you can use $s = vt$.

....

(c)   the time when B overtakes A.   **(5)**

> **Problem solving**   Find the time when the cars are the same distance from O.

....

....

....

....

....

Motion under gravity

Guided 1 A ball is projected vertically upwards with speed $21 \, \text{m s}^{-1}$ from a point A, which is $1.5 \, \text{m}$ above the ground. After projection, the ball moves freely under gravity until it reaches the ground. Modelling the ball as a particle, find

(a) the greatest height above A reached by the ball **(3)**

$s = ? \qquad u = \text{.........} \qquad v = 0 \qquad a = -9.8 \qquad \cancel{t = ?}$

$v^2 = u^2 + 2as \quad \text{so} \quad 0^2 = \text{.........}^2 - 2 \times 9.8 \times h$

$h = \text{..}$

> Remember that at the greatest height, $v = 0$. When travelling upwards, acceleration is negative and due to gravity, so use $a = -9.8 \, \text{m s}^{-2}$.

(b) the speed of the ball as it reaches the ground **(3)**

$s = -1.5 \qquad u = 21 \qquad v = ? \qquad a = -9.8 \qquad \cancel{t = ?}$

$v^2 = u^2 + 2as \quad \text{so} \quad v^2 = 21^2 + \text{.........} = \text{.........}$

$\text{so } v = \text{.........} \, \text{m s}^{-1}$

> Remember that the ball starts $1.5 \, \text{m}$ above the ground.

> Upwards is positive so s and a will both be negative.

(c) the time between the instant when the ball is projected from A and the instant when the ball reaches the ground. **(4)**

$\cancel{s = ?} \qquad u = 21 \qquad v = \text{..............} \qquad a = -9.8 \qquad t = ?$

$v = u + at$

> Upwards is positive so v will be negative.

....

....

Guided 2 A firework rocket starts from rest at ground level and moves vertically. In the first $4 \, \text{s}$ of its motion, the rocket rises $50 \, \text{m}$. The rocket is modelled as a particle moving with constant acceleration $a \, \text{m s}^{-2}$. Find

(a) the value of a **(2)**

> Use $s = ut + \frac{1}{2}at^2$.

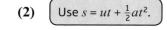

$s = \text{.........} \qquad u = 0 \qquad \cancel{v = ?} \qquad a = ? \qquad t = \text{.........}$

....

....

(b) the speed of the rocket $4 \, \text{s}$ after it has left the ground. **(2)**

> Use $v = u + at$.

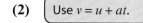

....

....

After $4 \, \text{s}$, the rocket burns out. The motion of the rocket is now modelled as that of a particle moving freely under gravity.

(c) Find the height of the rocket above the ground $7 \, \text{s}$ after it has left the ground. **(4)**

> Consider motion from $t = 4$ to $t = 7$; use $s = ut + \frac{1}{2}at^2$.

....

....

....

....

Forces

Guided   **1**   A breakdown van of mass 2500 kg is towing a car of mass 1500 kg along a straight horizontal road. The two vehicles are joined by a tow-bar which remains parallel to the road. The van and the car experience constant resistances to motion of magnitudes 900 N and 250 N respectively. There is a constant driving force acting on the van of 2750 N. Find

> Draw a clear diagram to help you see what is going on. Consider the **resultant** force in the direction of motion.

(a) the magnitude of the acceleration of the van and the car   **(3)**

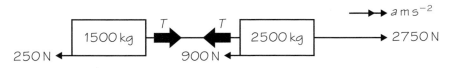

Van and car: $2750 - \ldots\ldots - \ldots\ldots = (2500 + 1500)a$

....

....

> Consider the breakdown van and car as a single system and apply $F = ma$. The two tensions in the tow-bar cancel out because they are equal and opposite.

(b) the tension in the tow-bar.   **(4)**

Car: $T - \ldots\ldots = 1500a$

> Consider the forces acting on the car and apply $F = ma$.

....

....

....

2   A man of mass 85 kg travels in a lift of mass 900 kg to the top of a tall building. The lift starts from rest on the ground floor and moves vertically upwards with an acceleration of $3\,\text{m s}^{-2}$. It then moves with constant speed and finally decelerates with a constant deceleration of $2\,\text{m s}^{-2}$ before coming to rest at the top floor. The lift is pulled up by means of a vertical cable attached to the top of the lift. By modelling the cable as a light inextensible string, find

> The force due to gravity on a mass m kg is mg N. Take $g = 9.8\,\text{m s}^{-2}$.

(a) the tension in the cable when the lift is accelerating   **(3)**

....

....

....

....

(b) the magnitude of the force exerted by the lift on the man when the lift is decelerating.   **(3)**

....

....

....

....

Forces as vectors

Guided 1 Two forces, $(3\mathbf{i} - 6\mathbf{j})$ N and $(p\mathbf{i} + q\mathbf{j})$ N, act on a particle P of mass m kg. The resultant of the two forces is $\mathbf{R}$. Given that $\mathbf{R}$ acts in a direction which is parallel to the vector $(2\mathbf{i} - \mathbf{j})$

(a) find the angle between $\mathbf{R}$ and the vector $\mathbf{j}$ **(3)**

> Draw a sketch to make sure you calculate the correct angle.

$$\tan \theta = \frac{\cdots\cdots\cdots}{\cdots\cdots} \qquad \theta = \cdots\cdots$$

$$\text{angle} = 90 + \cdots\cdots = \cdots\cdots^{\circ}$$

(b) show that $p + 2q = 9$ **(4)**

> To find the resultant, add the **i** components and the **j** components.

....

....

2 A particle is acted upon by two forces $\mathbf{F_1}$ and $\mathbf{F_2}$, given by

$$\mathbf{F_1} = (2\mathbf{i} - 4\mathbf{j})\text{ N}$$

$$\mathbf{F_2} = (p\mathbf{i} + 2p\mathbf{j})\text{ N, where } p \text{ is a positive constant.}$$

(a) Find the angle between $\mathbf{F_2}$ and $\mathbf{i}$.   **(2)**

....

The resultant of $\mathbf{F_1}$ and $\mathbf{F_2}$ is $\mathbf{R}$. Given that $\mathbf{R}$ is parallel to $\mathbf{j}$

(b) find the value of p, and the resultant force $\mathbf{R}$.   **(4)**

....

....

3 Three forces $\mathbf{F_1}$, $\mathbf{F_2}$ and $\mathbf{F_3}$ act on a particle P.

$$\mathbf{F_1} = (-3\mathbf{i} + 4\mathbf{j})\text{ N}, \quad \mathbf{F_2} = (p\mathbf{i} - 10\mathbf{j})\text{ N} \text{ and } \mathbf{F_3} = (7\mathbf{i} + q\mathbf{j})\text{ N, where } p \text{ and } q \text{ are constants.}$$

(a) If particle P is in equilibrium, find the values of p and q.   **(3)**

....

....

....

(b) Force $\mathbf{F_3}$ is now removed. The resultant of $\mathbf{F_1}$ and $\mathbf{F_2}$ is $\mathbf{R}$. Find the magnitude of $\mathbf{R}$ and the angle it makes with the vector $\mathbf{i}$.   **(5)**

> Draw a sketch to make sure you calculate the correct angle.

....

....

....

....

....

Motion in 2D

1   A particle of mass 2.5 kg is moving under the action of a constant force of $(2\mathbf{i} - 3\mathbf{j})$ N.

   (a) Find the magnitude of the acceleration of the particle.   **(3)**

....

....

   (b) Find the angle that the acceleration of the particle makes with $\mathbf{j}$.   **(2)**

....

....

Guided   2   A ball P of mass 0.5 kg is at rest when it is acted on by a constant force $(4\mathbf{i} + 3\mathbf{j})$ N

   (a) Find the total distance travelled by the ball in the first 5 seconds of its motion.   **(4)**

$$F = ma$$

$$4\mathbf{i} + 3\mathbf{j} = 0.5a$$

$$a = ...$$

$$|a| = \sqrt{..............^2 + ...^2} = ...\,\mathrm{ms}^{-2}$$

$$s = ut + \frac{1}{2}at^2$$

$$= ....$$

$$= .... \text{ m}$$

> The ball starts from rest and the force is acting in a straight line. The ball is moving with constant acceleration, so you can use $s = ut + \frac{1}{2}at^2$ to find the distance travelled.

   At time $t = 5$ s, a second force of $(1.3\mathbf{i} - 0.5\mathbf{j})$N acts on the particle

   (b) Find the new acceleration of the particle.   **(4)**

....

....

....

3   A particle Q of mass 4 kg is at rest under the action of three forces $\mathbf{F}_1$, $\mathbf{F}_2$ and $\mathbf{F}_3$, where $\mathbf{F}_1 = (10\mathbf{i} + 3\mathbf{j})$ N.

   Force $\mathbf{F}_2$ is removed and the particle accelerates at a rate of $(3\mathbf{i} - \mathbf{j})\,\mathrm{m\,s}^{-2}$.
   Find force $\mathbf{F}_3$, giving your answer in the form $(p\mathbf{i} + q\mathbf{j})$ N   **(5)**

....

....

....

> **Problem solving** The particle is initially at rest so $\mathbf{F}_1 + \mathbf{F}_2 + \mathbf{F}_3 = 0$ and the force causing the acceleration is $\mathbf{F}_1 + \mathbf{F}_3$.

....

....

Pulleys

> **Guided**   1   The particles A and B have masses 4 kg and m kg respectively, where $m < 4$. They are attached to the ends of a light inextensible string. The string passes over a smooth pulley which is fixed. The particles are held in position with the string taut and the hanging parts of the string vertical, at a height of 3 m above the floor, as shown in the diagram. The particles are then released from rest and in the subsequent motion B does not reach the pulley. The initial acceleration of each particle has magnitude $\frac{4}{7}g$.

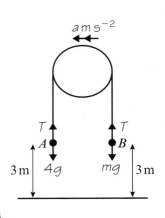

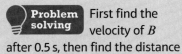

As $m < 4$, A will move down and B will move up. Apply $F = ma$ for each particle.

As the pulley is smooth, the tension in the string is the same for both particles.

(a) Find the tension in the string immediately after the particles are released and the value of m.   **(6)**

A: $4g - T = 4a$

....

....

....

....

When the particles have been moving for 0.5 s, the string breaks.

(b) Find the further time that elapses until B hits the floor.   **(9)**

($\uparrow$): $v = u + at =$ .... $=$ ....

($\uparrow$): $s = ut + \frac{1}{2}at^2 =$ .... $=$ ....

($\downarrow$): $s = ut + \frac{1}{2}at^2$

Problem solving   First find the velocity of B after 0.5 s, then find the distance travelled upwards in this time.

Problem solving   Finally, find the time taken for B to fall from the height where the string broke to the floor.

....

....

....

....

....

2   Two particles of masses 7 kg and 3 kg are connected by a light inextensible string passing over a smooth pulley. The system moves freely with the strings taut and vertical.
Find the acceleration of the particles and the tension in the string.   **(6)**

....

....

....

....

....

....

Connected particles

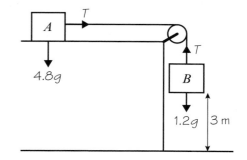

Guided   **1**   A particle, *A*, of mass 4.8 kg rests on a smooth horizontal table. It is connected by a light inextensible string passing over a smooth pulley fixed at the edge of the table to a particle, *B*, of mass 1.2 kg which hangs freely.

The system is released from rest with *B* at a height of 3 m above the ground.

(a) Find the acceleration of the system when it is released from rest and the tension in the string.   **(7)**

$F = ma$ for *A*: $T = 4.8a$

$F = ma$ for *B*: $1.2g -$ .... $=$ ....

Adding gives   .... $=$ .... so $a =$ .... $m s^{-2}$

Substituting gives $T = 4.8 \times$ .... $=$ .... N

(b) Find the speed with which **B** hits the ground and the time taken for this to happen.   **(6)**

$s = 3$ $u =$ .... $v =$ .... $a =$ .... $a =$ ....

....

....

....

....

> Choose *suvat* formulae to enable you to calculate *v* and *t*.

2   Two particles of masses 3 kg and 4 kg are connected by a light inextensible string passing over a smooth pulley. The system is released from rest with the strings taut and vertical.

After 3 seconds the 4 kg mass hits the ground.

(a) Given that in the subsequent motion the 3 kg mass does not reach the pulley, find the further time that elapses before the 3 kg mass reaches its greatest height.   **(7)**

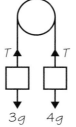

> **Problem solving**   First find the acceleration of the system. The 3 kg mass then moves freely under gravity.

....

....

....

....

....

....

(b) Find the **total** distance travelled by the 3 kg mass when it reaches its greatest height.   **(6)**

....

....

....

....

Combining techniques

1   A ball, *A*, of mass *m* kg, is held at rest on a rough horizontal table. It is attached to one end of a light inextensible string which passes over a smooth pulley at the edge of the table. The other end of the string is attached to a ball, *B*, of mass 3 kg hanging freely vertically below the pulley.

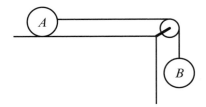

The system is released from rest with the string taut.

The resistance to the motion of *A* from the rough table is modelled as having constant magnitude 15.5 N.

(a) Given that ball *A* travels 1.8 m towards the pulley in 1.5 seconds and ball *B* does not reach the floor in this time, use the model to find the mass of ball *A*.   **(8)**

....

....

....

....

....

....

....

....

> Label the diagram with all the forces acting on the balls.

> Use a *suvat* equation to find the acceleration of the system.

> Use *F* = *ma* for both balls to find the value of *m*.

(b) Following the experiment, ball *A* is weighed and is found to have a mass of 5 kg. In light of this information

   (i) comment on the appropriateness of this model to find the mass of ball *A*,

   (ii) suggest one possible improvement to the model.   **(2)**

....

....

....

....

....

Variable acceleration 1

> **Guided**

1 A particle moves on the x-axis such that its distance from the origin, O, at time t seconds is given by
$$s = t^3 - 11t^2 + 24t, \ t \geqslant 0$$

(a) Sketch a distance–time graph for the particle. **(3)**

> This is a cubic graph with a positive coefficient of t^3.

$s = t(t^2 - 11t + 24) = t(\ldots\ldots)(\ldots\ldots)$

$s = 0$ when $t = \ldots\ldots$ and when $t = \ldots\ldots$

Graph crosses t-axis at $t = 0$, $t = \ldots\ldots$, $t = \ldots\ldots$

(b) Describe the motion of the particle during the first 8 seconds. **(3)**

> Consider changes of direction and times when the particle returns to O.

....

....

(c) Find the times when the particle is instantaneously at rest. **(4)**

> Instantaneously at rest means the velocity will be zero. Differentiate the expression for s.

....

....

(d) Find the furthest distance of the particle from O during the first 8 seconds. **(3)**

> Compare the values of s when the particle is instantaneously at rest.

....

....

2 A particle moves on the x-axis such that its distance from the origin, O, at time t seconds is given by
$$s = \frac{t^3 - 24t^2 + 144t}{9}, \ 0 \leqslant t \leqslant 12$$

(a) Sketch a distance–time graph for the particle. **(3)**

(b) Find the initial velocity of the particle. **(3)**

....

....

....

(c) Find the times when the particle is instantaneously at rest. **(3)**

....

....

(d) Find the maximum distance of the particle from O in the interval $0 \leqslant t \leqslant 12$ **(2)**

....

....

Variable acceleration 2

Guided **1** A particle, P, moves on the x-axis. At time t seconds, the velocity of P is $v\,\text{ms}^{-1}$, in the direction of x increasing, where

$$v = t^2 - 8t + 12, \quad t \geqslant 0$$

(a) Find the times when P is instantaneously at rest. **(3)**

P is instantaneously at rest when v = 0

$t^2 - 8t + 12 = 0$, (............)(............) $= 0$, so $t = $ .... and $t = $ ....

(b) Sketch the velocity–time graph of the particle and find its maximum speed in the first 4 seconds of the motion. **(4)**

> **Problem solving** Use the symmetry of the graph to find the value of t at the minimum point. Work out v and compare it with $12\,\text{m s}^{-1}$ at $t = 0$.

....
....
....

(c) Find the total distance travelled by P in the interval $0 \leqslant t \leqslant 5$ **(5)**

....
....

> Distance = area under a v-t graph. Use definite integration.

....
....

2 A particle, Q, moves on the x-axis such that its distance, in metres, from the origin, O, at time t seconds is given by $s = 8t - \frac{2}{3}t^3$, $t \geqslant 0$

(a) Find the initial velocity of the particle. **(2)**

....

(b) Show that Q changes direction between
$t = 0$ and $t = 4$ **(3)**

> **Problem solving** A change of direction means that Q will be instantaneously at rest during this time.

....
....
....

(c) Find the total distance travelled by Q in the interval $0 \leqslant t \leqslant 4$ **(3)**

> **Problem solving** Q oscillates both sides of O, so you need to consider distances travelled in both directions.

....
....
....

Deriving *suvat* equations

1 The diagram shows a velocity–time graph for a particle travelling in a straight line accelerating uniformly from velocity $U\,\mathrm{m\,s^{-1}}$ to velocity $V\,\mathrm{m\,s^{-1}}$ in time T seconds. The acceleration of the particle, $a\,\mathrm{m\,s^{-2}}$, is equal to the gradient of the graph.

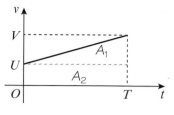

$$a = \frac{V - U}{T} \quad \text{so} \quad V = U + aT$$

(a) Show that the distance travelled, s, is given by $\left(\dfrac{U + V}{2}\right)T$ **(4)**

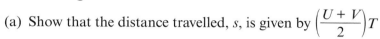

Distance travelled = area under graph so $s = A_1 + A_2$

$A_1 = \frac{1}{2} \times$ base $\times$ height $= \frac{1}{2} \times T \times (V - U)$ and $A_2 = U \times T$

So $s = \frac{1}{2}T(V - U) + UT = \frac{1}{2}TV -$ .... $+$ .... $=$ .... $=$ ....

(b) Use the two *suvat* equations above to derive the equations

    (i) $s = UT + \frac{1}{2}aT^2$ **(3)**   (ii) $V^2 = U^2 + 2as$ **(3)**

> Use algebra, involving substitution.

....

....

....

....

....

2 Points A and B are 720 m apart along a straight line.

A particle, P, travels from A to B. Its displacement from A is given by $s = 16t - 0.3t^2$, $t \geqslant 0$

A particle, Q, travels along the same straight line but in the opposite direction.

Q passes point B at time $t = 0$ with an initial velocity, towards A, of $5\,\mathrm{m\,s^{-1}}$ and a constant acceleration of $0.8\,\mathrm{m\,s^{-2}}$.

(a) Derive an expression, in terms of t, for the distance travelled towards A by particle Q.   **(4)**

    Do **not** use the kinematics formulae to derive this expression.

....

....

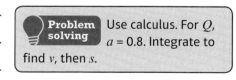

Problem solving   Use calculus. For Q, $a = 0.8$. Integrate to find v, then s.

....

(b) Find the time taken for the particles to meet.   **(4)**

....

Problem solving   Use total distance = 720 m.

....

....

(c) Find the distance from A when the particles meet.   **(2)**

....

....

You are the examiner!

Checking through your work is a key skill for AS maths. Have a look at pages 94 and 95 of the *Revision Guide*, then practise with these questions. There are full worked solutions on page 116.

1   A train travels between two stations A and B which are 23.1 km apart. It starts from rest at A and takes $3\frac{1}{2}$ minutes to accelerate uniformly to a speed of $35\,\text{m s}^{-1}$.

It maintains this speed for a period of time and then decelerates uniformly to come to rest at B. The distance travelled when decelerating is 1575 m.

(a) Sketch a velocity–time graph to illustrate the motion of the train.   **(3)**

(b) Find the time taken, in minutes, for the journey between the two stations.   **(5)**

....

....

....

....

....

2   Three forces $\mathbf{F}_1$, $\mathbf{F}_2$ and $\mathbf{F}_3$ act on a particle P.

   $\mathbf{F}_1 = (2p\mathbf{i} - \mathbf{j})\,\text{N}$, $\mathbf{F}_2 = (q\mathbf{i} - 5p\mathbf{j})\,\text{N}$ and $\mathbf{F}_3 = (4\mathbf{i} - 7q\mathbf{j})\,\text{N}$, where p and q are constants.

(a) If particle P is in equilibrium, find the values of p and q.   **(5)**

....

....

....

....

....

Force $\mathbf{F}_3$ is now removed. The resultant of $\mathbf{F}_1$ and $\mathbf{F}_2$ is $\mathbf{R}$.

(b) Find the magnitude of $\mathbf{R}$ and the angle it makes with the vector $\mathbf{j}$.   **(5)**

....

....

....

....

....

You are the examiner!

Checking through your work is a key skill for AS maths. Have a look at pages 94 and 95 of the *Revision Guide*, then practise with these questions. There are full worked solutions on page 116.

3   Two particles, A and B, of masses 4 kg and 6 kg respectively, are connected by a light inextensible string which passes over a smooth pulley.

The system is released from rest with the strings taut and vertical.

(a) Find the acceleration of the system when it is released from rest and the tension in the string.   **(6)**

....

....

....

(b) Find the speed of the particles 1.5 seconds after the system is released from rest.   **(2)**

....

After 1.5 seconds, the string breaks. Given that in the subsequent motion particle A does not reach the pulley,

(c) find the further time that elapses before particle A reaches its greatest height   **(2)**

....

....

(d) find the **total** distance travelled by particle A when it reaches its greatest height.   **(5)**

....

....

....

4   A particle moves along the x-axis.

The acceleration of the particle, in m s^{-2}, at time t seconds is given by $a = 4 - 2t$.

The initial velocity of the particle as it passes the origin, O, is 5 m s^{-1} in the positive x direction.

(a) Find the velocity of the particle as a function of t.   **(3)**

....

....

(b) Find the greatest speed of the particle.   **(2)**

....

(c) Find the distance travelled by the particle from the time when it is travelling at its greatest speed to the time when it comes to instantaneous rest.   **(7)**

....

....

....

....

Pure Mathematics
Calculators may be used in this practice paper.
Time: 2 hours
Total marks: 100
You may use the Mathematical Formulae and Statistical Tables booklet which is available from the Edexcel website.

1 Express 32^{4x+1} in the form 2^y, stating y in terms of x. **(2)**

2 The position vectors of A and B are $-3\mathbf{i} + 2\mathbf{j}$ and $4\mathbf{i} + 6\mathbf{j}$ respectively.
   (a) Find $\overrightarrow{AB}$ **(2)**
   (b) Find the exact value of $|\overrightarrow{AB}|$. **(2)**

3 Find the set of values for which $2x^2 + x > 28$ **(4)**

4 Show that $\dfrac{40 - \sqrt{180}}{4\sqrt{5} - 3}$ can be written in the form $a\sqrt{b}$ where a and b are integers. **(5)**

5 $f(x) = 4x^2 - 1 - \dfrac{2}{x^3}, \quad x > 0$

   Show that $\displaystyle\int_1^{\sqrt{2}} f(x)\,dx = \dfrac{5}{6}(2\sqrt{2} - 1)$ **(5)**

6 Prove, from first principles, that the derivative of $4x^2 + 7x$ is $8x + 7$ **(4)**

7

Find the area of triangle ABC. **(5)**

8 Solve, for $-180° \leqslant x \leqslant 180°$, giving your answers in degrees to 1 decimal place.
      $5\sin(x - 45°) = 2$ **(4)**

   (Solutions based entirely on graphical or numerical methods are not acceptable).

9 $f(x) = 3x^3 + 2x^2 - 23x + k$
   (a) Given that $(x + 2)$ is a factor of $f(x)$, find the value of k. **(2)**
   (b) Factorise $f(x)$ completely. **(4)**

10 (a) Find the first four terms of the binomial expansion, in ascending powers of x, of
      $\left(1 - \dfrac{x}{3}\right)^9$, giving each term in its simplest form. **(4)**
   (b) Use your expansion to estimate the value of $(0.996)^9$, giving your answer to 4 d.p. **(3)**

11 A circle, C, has the equation $x^2 + y^2 - 10x + 8y - 59 = 0$

    (a) Write down the coordinates of the centre of the circle. **(2)**

    The tangent to C at the point $(-3, 2)$ cuts the x-axis at the point P and the y-axis at the point Q.

    (b) Find the area of triangle OPQ, where O is the origin. **(6)**

12 (a) Given that $2\log_2(x - 4) - \log_2(3x - 4) = 1$, show that $x^2 - 14x + 24 = 0$ **(5)**

    (b) Hence, or otherwise, solve

$$2\log_2(x - 4) - \log_2(3x - 4) = 1$$ **(3)**

13 The line L_1 has equation $3y + 5x - 4 = 0$

    The line L_2 is perpendicular to L_1 and passes through the point $A(-2, 6)$.

    (a) Find the equation of L_2, giving your answer in the form $ax + by + c = 0$, where a, b and c are integers. **(4)**

    L_2 crosses the x-axis at the point B.

    (b) Find the exact length of AB. **(4)**

14 The line $y = 5x - k$, where k is a constant, is a tangent to the curve $y = kx^2 - 7x + 5$

    Find the two possible values of k. **(7)**

15 The curve C has equation $\dfrac{4}{x^2} - 1$ $(x \neq 0)$ and the line L has equation $y = 2x + 5$

    (a) On a single diagram, sketch and clearly label the graphs of C and L, showing any points of intersection with the coordinate axes. **(5)**

    (b) State the equations of the asymptotes to the curve C. **(2)**

    (c) Find the exact x-coordinates of the points of intersection of $y = \dfrac{4}{x^2} - 1$ and $y = 2x + 5$ **(5)**

16 A closed cuboidal box has a rectangular base of length $2x$ cm and width x cm, and a height of y cm.

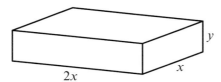

    The box holds 20 litres.

    (a) Show that the total surface area, A cm^2, is given by $A = 4x^2 + \dfrac{60\,000}{x}$ **(3)**

    (b) Use calculus to find the minimum value of A. Give your answer to 3 significant figures. **(6)**

    (c) Justify that the value of A you have found is a minimum. **(2)**

Statistics and Mechanics
Calculators may be used in this practice paper.
Time: 1 hour 15 minutes
Total marks: 60
You may use the Mathematical Formulae and Statistical Tables booklet which is available from the Edexcel website.

Section A: Statistics
Answer ALL questions

1. A teacher measured the length of the left foot, l cm, and the height, h cm, of a sample of 10 students in her class. The lengths, l cm, ranged from 22 cm to 28 cm. The equation of the regression line of h on l was calculated as $h = 98.4 + 1.67l$

   (a) Comment on the reliability of using this regression equation to estimate the height of a student whose left foot measured:
       (i) 26 cm **(1)**
       (ii) 30 cm **(1)**

   (b) Paul used the regression equation to estimate the length of the left foot of a student who was 170 cm tall.

       Explain fully why this regression model would not be suitable for this prediction. **(2)**

2. The mark, x, scored by each student in an exam, is coded using $y = 1.3x - 15$

   The coded marks have a mean of 62.1 and a standard deviation of 6.17.

   Find the mean and the standard deviation of the original marks. **(4)**

3. The Venn diagram shows the probabilities of a group of people watching TV programmes A, B and C.

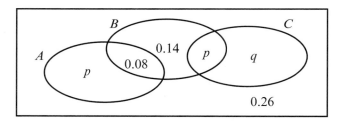

   (a) Given that the probability of watching C is twice the probability of watching A, find the values of p and q. **(4)**

   (b) State, giving a reason, whether or not the events 'watching B' and 'watching C' are statistically independent. Show your working clearly. **(3)**

4   The partially completed histogram and the partially completed table show the times, to the nearest minute, that a random sample of runners took to complete a half marathon.

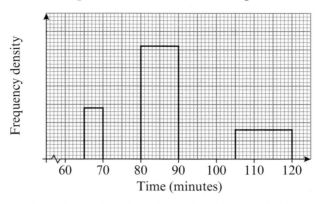

Time, t (minutes)	Number of runners
$65 < t \leqslant 70$	7
$70 < t \leqslant 80$	20
$80 < t \leqslant 90$	
$90 < t \leqslant 105$	45
$105 < t \leqslant 120$	

(a) Complete the histogram and find the missing numbers in the frequency table. **(4)**

(b) Estimate the percentage of runners who completed the half marathon in a time between 76 and 110 minutes. **(3)**

5   A magazine article states that 25% of people eat at least five portions of fruit and veg every day. Emily says that this can be modelled by the binomial distribution B(n, 0.25) and she decides to test her theory on the 24 students in her maths set.

Using the distribution model suggested by Emily, find the probability that, of the students in her maths set,

(a) fewer than six of them eat at least five portions of fruit and veg every day **(1)**

(b) at least four, but fewer than ten, of them eat at least five portions of fruit and veg every day. **(2)**

Emily's teacher thinks that more than 25% people eat at least five portions of fruit and veg every day. He suggests that Emily asks the 20 students in another maths set.

She finds that 8 of them say they eat at least five portions of fruit and veg every day.

(c) Using a 5% significance level, find if there is sufficient evidence to support the teacher's theory. State your hypotheses clearly. **(5)**

Section B: Mechanics
Answer ALL questions

Unless otherwise indicated, whenever a numerical value of g is required, take $g = 9.8\,\text{m s}^{-2}$ and give your answer to either 2 significant figures or 3 significant figures.

6   A car is travelling at $20\,\text{m s}^{-1}$ when the driver sees an incident in the road and has to perform an emergency stop.

The car travels for 14 metres before the driver applies the brakes.

After the brakes are applied, the car then slows down to a stop with constant deceleration.

The total time taken from the driver seeing the incident to the car stopping is 3.9 seconds

   (a) Sketch a velocity−time graph for the car. (2)

   (b) Find the total distance travelled. (3)

   (c) Work out the deceleration of the car. (2)

7   A particle, P, moves on the x-axis in the positive direction. At time t seconds ($t \geqslant 0$), the acceleration of P is $(2t + 2.5)\,\text{m s}^{-2}$.

When $t = 0$, the velocity of P is $3\,\text{m s}^{-1}$.

Find the time, T seconds, when the velocity of P is $9\,\text{m s}^{-1}$. (6)

8   A ball is thrown vertically upwards, with speed $u\,\text{m s}^{-1}$, from a point P at a height h metres above the ground.

The ball hits the ground 1.5 seconds later. The speed of the ball immediately before it hits the ground is $10.8\,\text{m s}^{-1}$.

   (a) Show that $u = 3.9$ (3)

   (b) Find the value of h. (3)

   (c) State two modelling assumptions made when calculating your answers. (2)

9   A truck of mass $3800\,\text{kg}$ is pulling a trailer of mass $m\,\text{kg}$ along a rough horizontal road. They are connected by a tow rope, modelled as a light inextensible string.

The trailer has a resistance to motion, which can be modelled as a constant force, of $1260\,\text{N}$. The truck has a resistance to motion which can be modelled as a constant force, of $x\,\text{N}$ per tonne.

The truck generates a driving force of $6000\,\text{N}$ which causes the truck and trailer to accelerate at $0.55\,\text{m s}^{-2}$.

When they are travelling at $18\,\text{m s}^{-1}$, the tow rope breaks. The trailer comes to rest in 3.2 seconds.

   (a) Find the deceleration of the trailer after the tow rope breaks. (2)

   (b) Hence find the mass of the trailer, $m\,\text{kg}$. (2)

   (c) Find the value of x. (5)

Answers

Worked solutions have been provided for all Guided questions. These are marked with a . Short answers have been provided for all other questions.

1. Index laws

1 5^{-3}

 2 $\sqrt{3}\left(27^{\frac{2}{3}}\right) = 3^{\frac{1}{2}} \times \left(27^{\frac{1}{3}}\right)^2 = 3^{\frac{1}{2}} \times 3^2 = 3^{\frac{5}{2}}$

3 $6x^{\frac{1}{4}}$

4 $5x^{\frac{2}{3}}$

 5 $\dfrac{\left(3x^{\frac{1}{2}}\right)^3}{9x^3} = \dfrac{27x^{\frac{3}{2}}}{9x^3} = 3x^{-\frac{3}{2}} = \dfrac{3}{x^{\frac{3}{2}}}$

6 $3x^{-\frac{1}{2}} - x; \ p = -\frac{1}{2}, q = 1$

7 $x = \frac{1}{2}$

8 $x = \frac{1}{2}$

9 $3x^{-\frac{5}{2}} + 2x^{-\frac{9}{2}}; \ p = -\frac{5}{2}, q = -\frac{9}{2}$

2. Expanding and factorising

 1 $(x - 1)(x + 2)^2 = (x - 1)(x^2 + 4x + 4)$
$= x^3 + 4x^2 + 4x - x^2 - 4x - 4 = x^3 + 3x^2 - 4$

 2 $x^3 - 9x = x(x^2 - 9) = x(x + 3)(x - 3)$

3 $x^3 - 3x^2 - 6x + 8$

4 $x(x + 5)(x - 1)$

5 $(2 - 3\sqrt{x})(2 - 3\sqrt{x}) = 4 - 6\sqrt{x} - 6\sqrt{x} + 9x$
$= 4 - 12\sqrt{x} + 9x$

$k = 12$

6 (a) $x(x^2 - x - 6)$ (b) $x(x - 3)(x + 2)$

3. Surds

1 $6\sqrt{2}$

 2 $\sqrt{18} + \sqrt{50} = \sqrt{9 \times 2} + \sqrt{25 \times 2}$
$= 3 \times \sqrt{2} + 5 \times \sqrt{2} = 8\sqrt{2}$

 3 $\dfrac{\sqrt{5} + 3}{\sqrt{5} - 2} = \dfrac{(\sqrt{5} + 3)(\sqrt{5} + 2)}{(\sqrt{5} - 2)(\sqrt{5} + 2)}$
$= \dfrac{5 + 5\sqrt{5} + 6}{5 - 4} = \dfrac{11 + 5\sqrt{5}}{1} = 11 + 5\sqrt{5}$

4 $12\sqrt{3}$

5 $a = 2, b = 3$

6 $c = 7, d = 52$

7 $12\sqrt{5} - 27$

4. Quadratic equations

1 $x = -2, x = \frac{4}{3}$

 2 (a) $x^2 - 10x + 15 = (x - 5)^2 - 25 + 15 = (x - 5)^2 - 10$
(b) $(x - 5)^2 - 10 = 0$
$(x - 5)^2 = 10$
$(x - 5) = \pm\sqrt{10}$
$x = 5 \pm \sqrt{10}$
$c = 5, d = 1$

3 $p = -4, q = 10$

4 $a = 3, b = 1, c = 2$

5. Functions and roots

 1 Let $u = x^2$, then $2u^2 - u - 28 = 0$, $(2u + 7)(u - 4) = 0$
So $2u + 7 = 0$ or $u - 4 = 0$, giving $u = -\frac{7}{2}$ or $u = 4$
So using $u = x^2$, $x^2 = -\frac{7}{2}$, but x^2 cannot be negative
So $x^2 = 4$, giving $x = 2$ or $x = -2$

2 $x = \frac{1}{2}, x = -2$

3 $x = \frac{9}{4}, x = 25$

4 $x = 64$

5 $x = -\dfrac{\sqrt{3}}{2}$

6 $x = 9 - 4\sqrt{2}$

6. Sketching quadratics

 1 When $x = 0$, $y = (0 - 3)(0 + 2) = -6$
When $y = 0$, $0 = (x - 3)(x + 2)$
so $x = 3$ or $x = -2$

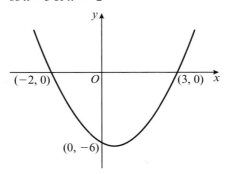

 2 The coordinates of the vertex are $(-3, 4)$
When $x = 0$, $y = (0 + 3)^2 + 4 = 13$

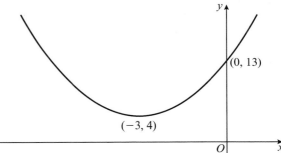

3

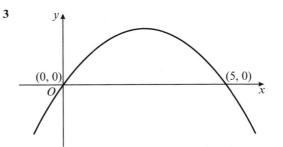

4 (a) $3(x - 2)^2 + 5$
(b)

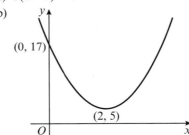

(c) No points of intersection with the x-axis.

7. The discriminant

 1 $a = 1$, $b = -2p$, $c = p$
$b^2 - 4ac = (-2p)^2 - 4 \times 1 \times p = 4p^2 - 4p$
$4p^2 - 4p = 0$
$4p(p - 1) = 0$
$p(p - 1) = 0$
$p = 1$ (as $p \neq 0$)

 2 $3x^2 + kx - 5 - k = 0$
$a = 3$, $b = k$, $c = -5 - k$
$b^2 - 4ac = (k)^2 - 4 \times 3 \times (-5 - k) = k^2 + 12k + 60$
For no real roots, $b^2 - 4ac < 0$ so $k^2 + 12k + 60 < 0$

3 -19

4 (a) $p^2 + 4p + 16$

(b) $p^2 + 4p + 16 = (p + 2)^2 + 12$ giving $a = 2$, $b = 12$

(c) $(p + 2)^2 \geqslant 0$ for all values of p,
so $(p + 2)^2 + 12 > 0$,
so there are real different roots for all values of p

8. Modelling with quadratics

 1 (a) Relative speed upstream
= speed of boat − speed of current = $u - 5.5$ km/h

Time to travel upstream, $t_1 = \dfrac{\text{distance}}{\text{relative speed}}$

$= \dfrac{30}{u - 5.5}$ hours

Relative speed downstream = $u + 5.5$ km/h

so $t_2 = \dfrac{\text{distance}}{\text{relative speed}} = \dfrac{30}{u + 5.5}$ hours

(b) $\dfrac{30}{u - 5.5} + \dfrac{30}{u + 5.5} = 3$,

$10(u + 5.5) + 10(u - 5.5) = (u + 5.5)(u - 5.5)$
$10u + 55 + 10u - 55 = u^2 - 30.25$
so $u^2 - 20u - 30.25 = 0$

(c) $u = 21.4127$ m s^{-1}, $t_1 = 113$ minutes, $t_2 = 67$ minutes

2 (a) 2.86 seconds

(b) Maximum height = 10.22... metres

9. Simultaneous equations

 1 $y = x - 3$ ③
$x^2 - 2(x - 3) = 6$
$x^2 - 2x + 6 = 6$
$x^2 - 2x = 0$
$x(x - 2) = 0$
$x = 0$, $y = -3$ or $x = 2$, $y = -1$

2 (a) $x(x + 8) + 3x^2 = 16$ gives $4x^2 + 8x - 16 = 0$
so $x^2 + 2x - 4 = 0$

(b) $x = -1 \pm \sqrt{5}$, $y = 7 \pm \sqrt{5}$

3 (a) $(4, -3)$

(b)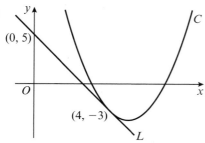

Curve crosses x-axis at 3 and 7. L is a tangent to the curve at the point $(4, -3)$

10. Inequalities

 1 (a) $2x - 6 < 4 - 3x$
$5x < 10$ so $x < 2$

(b) $(2x - 5)(2 + x) = 0$
So $x = -2$ or $x = \frac{5}{2}$
For $y < 0$, $-2 < x < \frac{5}{2}$

(c) $-2 < x < 2$

2 (a) $x < 3$ and $x > 5$

(b)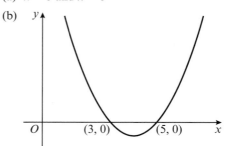

The region $x \leqslant 3$ and $x \geqslant 5$ is where the curve is above the x-axis

3 (a) $(2k)^2 - 4(3 - 2k) > 0$ gives $k^2 + 2k - 3 > 0$

(b) $k < -3$ and $k > 1$

4 $-3 < p < 2$

11. Inequalities on graphs

 1 (a) $2x^2 + 3x - 5 = 0$, $(2x + 5)(x - 1) = 0$, $x = -2.5$ and $x = 1$
When $x = 0$, $y = -5$
For $y = 2x + 1$, graph crosses y-axis when $x = 0$, so $y = 1$
Graph crosses x-axis when $y = 0$, so $x = -0.5$

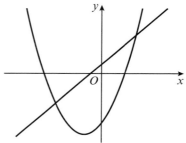

(b) $2x^2 + 3x - 5 = 2x + 1$, $2x^2 + x - 6 = 0$,
$(2x - 3)(x + 2) = 0$, $x = 1.5$ and $x = -2$
When $x = 1.5$, $y = 4$ and when $x = -2$, $y = -3$

(c) $x \leqslant -2$ and $x \geqslant 1.5$

2 (a) $(-5, 6)$ and $(2, -8)$

(b)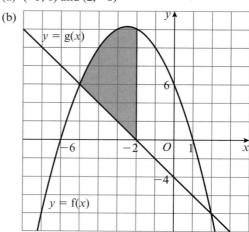

(c) $-5 < x < 2$

(d) See shaded area on graph above.

12. Cubic and quartic graphs

G 1 When $y = 0$, $0 = x(x + 2)(x - 5)$
so $x = -2$ or $x = 0$ or $x = 5$

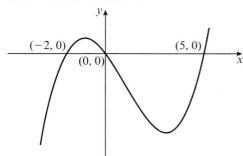

G 2 When $y = 0$, $0 = (x + 1)^2(3 - x)$ so $x = -1$ or $x = 3$
When $x = 0$, $y = (0 + 1)^2(3 - 0) = 3$

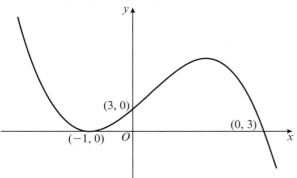

3

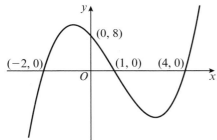

4

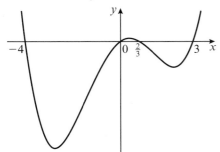

13. Transformations 1

G 1

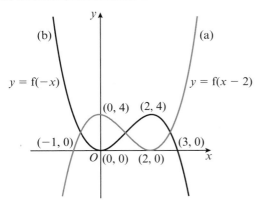

G 2 (a)

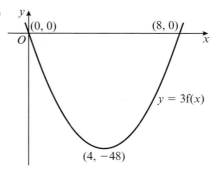

(b)

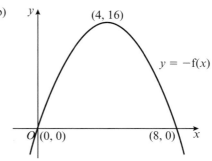

(c)

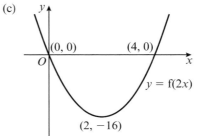

(d) $k = 4$

14. Transformations 2

G 1 (a)

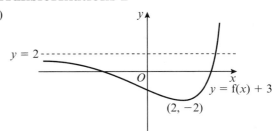

(b)

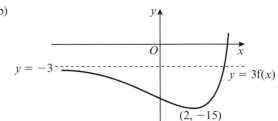

(c)

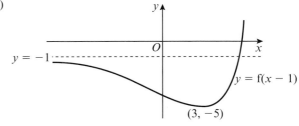

Answers

2 (a)

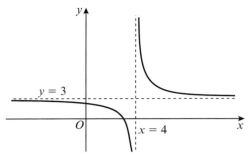

(b) $f(x - 3) = \dfrac{3(x - 3)}{(x - 3) - 1} = \dfrac{3(x - 3)}{x - 4}$

(0, 2.25) and (3, 0)

15. Reciprocal graphs

1 (a)

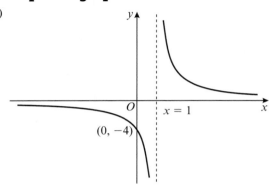

(b) $x = 1$ and $y = 0$

2 (a)

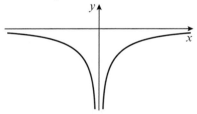

(b)

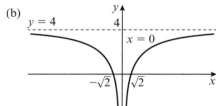

(c)

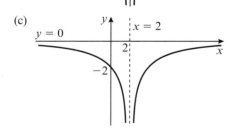

16. Points of intersection

G 1 (a)

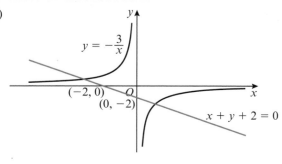

(b) $y = -x - 2$

$-\dfrac{3}{x} = -x - 2$ so $-3 = -x^2 - 2x$

$x^2 + 2x - 3 = 0$

$(x + 3)(x - 1) = 0$

$(-3, 1)$ and $(1, -3)$

2 (a)

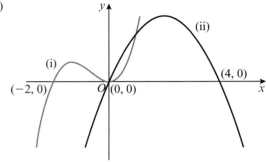

(b) $(0, 0)$ and $(1, 3)$ and $(-4, -32)$

17. Equations of lines

1 $y = 7 - 3 \times 3 = -2$

G 2 $7y = 3 - 2x$

$y = \dfrac{3}{7} - \dfrac{2}{7}x$

Gradient $= -\dfrac{2}{7}$

G 3 $x_1 = 3$, $y_1 = -2$, $m = -\dfrac{1}{3}$

$y - (-2) = -\dfrac{1}{3}(x - 3)$

$3(y + 2) = -1(x - 3)$

$3y + 6 = -x + 3$

$y = -\dfrac{1}{3}x - 1$

G 4 (a) $x_1 = -2$, $y_1 = 1$, $x_2 = 6$, $y_2 = -2$

$m = \dfrac{y_2 - y_1}{x_2 - x_1} = \dfrac{-2 - 1}{6 + 2} = \dfrac{-3}{8}$

(b) $y - 1 = -\dfrac{3}{8}(x + 2)$

$8(y - 1) = -3(x + 2)$

$8y - 8 = -3x - 6$

$3x + 8y - 2 = 0$

5 (a) $p = 1$ (b) $4x + 3y - 17 = 0$

18. Parallel and perpendicular

G 1 (a) $y = 4 - 3 \times 3 = -5$, so $(3, -5)$ lies on L

(b) Gradient of $L = -3$

Gradient of perpendicular line $= \dfrac{1}{3}$

Equation of perpendicular line through $(3, -5)$ is

$y + 5 = \dfrac{1}{3}(x - 3)$

$3y + 15 = x - 3$

$x - 3y - 18 = 0$

G 2 (a) Coordinates of midpoint are $\left(\dfrac{-2 + 6}{2}, \dfrac{5 + 3}{2} \right) = (2, 4)$

(b) $4x - y - 4 = 0$

3 $y = \dfrac{4}{3}x + \dfrac{5}{3}$

19. Lengths and areas

1 $p = 4$

G 2 (a) $x + 3(x + 1) - 15 = 0$

$x + 3x + 3 - 15 = 0$

$4x = 12$

$x = 3$

Coordinates are $(3, 4)$

(b) 32

3 l_2 has equation $2x + 3y = 14$

Point of intersection is $(-2, 6)$

Area $= 39$

20. Equation of a circle

1 $(x - 4)^2 + (y + 1)^2 = 6^2$

⊳G 2 (a) $r = \sqrt{(-1 - 2)^2 + (7 - 3)^2} = 5$
$(x - 2)^2 + (y - 3)^2 = r^2$
$(x - 2)^2 + (y - 3)^2 = 25$

(b) $(5 - 2)^2 + (7 - 3)^2 = 3^2 + 4^2 = 9 + 16 = 25$
so $(5, 7)$ lies on C.

3 $(x - 1)^2 + (y - 8)^2 = 25$

4 (a) Centre $(-1, 3)$; radius 4

(b) $(-1 + \sqrt{7}, 0); (-1 - \sqrt{7}, 0); (0, 3 + \sqrt{15}); (0, 3 - \sqrt{15})$

21. Circle properties

1 Equation is $(x + 2)^2 + (y - 3)^2 = 25$;
centre $(-2, 3)$, radius 5
Midpoint of PQ is $(-2, 3)$ so PQ is diameter.

⊳G 2 (a) Gradient of tangent $= \frac{3}{5}$
Gradient of line through P and $Q = -\frac{5}{3}$
Equation of line is $y - y_1 = m(x - x_1)$
$y - 7 = -\frac{5}{3}(x - 1)$
$3y - 21 = -5x + 5$
$5x + 3y - 26 = 0$

(b) $Q (4, 2)$

3 (a) $P (22, 0); Q (0, 11)$

(b) 165

22. Circles and lines

⊳G 1 Substitute $y = 2x - 3$ into the equation of the circle.
$(x + 3)^2 + (2x - 3 + 2)^2 = 26 \Rightarrow (x + 3)^2 + (2x - 1)^2 = 26$
$x^2 + 6x + 9 + 4x^2 - 4x + 1 = 26$
$5x^2 + 2x - 16 = 0$
$(5x - 8)(x + 2) = 0$, so $x = 1.6$ and $x = -2$
When $x = 1.6$, $y = 2 \times 1.6 - 3 = 0.2$,
and when $x = -2$, $y = 2(-2) - 3 = -7$
$(-2, -7)$ and $(\frac{8}{5}, \frac{1}{5})$

2 $k < -2\sqrt{5}$ and $k > 2\sqrt{5}$

3 $k = 10\sqrt{2}$

23. The factor theorem

⊳G 1 (a) $f(x) = 2x^3 - 3x^2 - 11x + 6$
$f(-2) = 2(-2)^3 - 3(-2)^2 - 11(-2) + 6$
$= -16 - 12 + 22 + 6$
$= 0$
So $(x + 2)$ is a factor.

(b)

$$
\begin{array}{r|rrrr}
-2 & 2 & -3 & -11 & 6 \\
   &   & -4 & 14 & -6 \\
\hline
   & 2 & -7 & 3 & 0
\end{array}
$$

$f(x) = (x + 2)(2x^2 - 7x + 3)$
$= (x + 2)(2x - 1)(x - 3)$

2 (a) $(x + 6)(2x + 1)(x - 2)$

(b) $(x - 4)(3x - 4)(x + 2)$

(c) $(x - 3)(3x - 1)(2x - 3)$

3 (a) $c = -24$

(b) $(x - 4)(2x + 3)(x + 2)$

4 (a) $(x - 2)(3x - 1)(x + 5)$

(b) $x = 2, x = \frac{1}{3}, x = -5$

24. The binomial expansion

⊳G 1 $a = 3 \qquad b = -2x \qquad n = 5$
$(3 - 2x)^5 = (3)^5 + \binom{5}{1}(3)^4(-2x) + \binom{5}{2}(3)^3(-2x)^2 + \ldots$
$= 243 + [5 \times 81 \times (-2x)] + [10 \times 27 \times 4x^2] + \ldots$
$\approx 243 - 810x + 1080x^2$

⊳G 2 (a) $a = 1 \qquad b = px \qquad n = 9$
$(1 + px)^9 = 1^9 + \binom{9}{1}1^8px + \binom{9}{2}1^7(px)^2 + \ldots$
$\approx 1 + 9px + 36p^2x^2$

(b) $(1 + px)^9 = 1 + 9px + 36p^2x^2 + \ldots$
$9p = q \qquad 36p^2 = 20q$
$36p^2 = 20 \times 9p$
$p^2 = 5p$
$p = 5, q = 45$

3 $16\,384 - 86\,016x + 193\,536x^2$

4 (a) $64 + 576x + 2160x^2$

(b) $64 + 560x + 2016x^2$

25. Solving binomial problems

⊳G 1 $n = 12 \qquad r = 7 \qquad a = 4 \qquad b = -\frac{x}{2}$
$\binom{12}{7}4^5\left(-\frac{x}{2}\right)^7 = 792 \times 1024 \times \left(-\frac{x^7}{128}\right) = -6336x^7$
Coefficient $= -6336$

⊳G 2 $1 + \frac{x}{2} = 1.005, \frac{x}{2} = 0.005, x = 0.01$
$(1.005)^8 \approx 1 + 4(0.01) + 7(0.01)^2 + 7(0.01)^3$
$\approx 1.040\,71$ (5 d.p.)

3 (a) $1 + \frac{9x}{4} + \frac{9x^2}{4} + \frac{21x^3}{16}$

(b) 1.2488

4 (a) $1 - 14x + 84x^2 - 280x^3$

(b) 0.8681

(c) $(1 + x)(1 - 14x) \approx 1 - 14x + x = 1 - 13x$

26. Proof

⊳G 1 (a) $\frac{(n + 1)}{(n + 2)}$

(b) Difference $= \frac{(n + 1)}{(n + 2)} - \frac{n}{(n + 1)} = \frac{(n + 1)^2 - n(n + 2)}{(n + 2)(n + 1)}$
$= \frac{n^2 + 2n + 1 - n^2 - 2n}{(n + 2)(n + 1)}$
$= \frac{1}{(n + 2)(n + 1)}$ as required.

(c) 11th and 12th terms

2 $(2n + 1)^3 - (2n - 1)^3 = (8n^3 + 12n^2 + 6n + 1)$
$- (8n^3 + 12n^2 + 6n - 1)$
$= 24n^2 + 2$
Mean of $(2n + 1)$ and $(2n - 1) = 2n$
$(2n)^2 = 4n^2, 6 \times 4n^2 = 24n^2$ as required

3 (a)

n	1	2	3	4	5	6	7
$2n^2 - n + 1$	2	7	16	29	46	67	92

i.e. never divisible by 11

(b) Trying $n = 2, 3, 5$ and 7 gives a prime number, but
$n = 11$ gives 155, which is divisible by 5.

4 $3n^2 + 6n = 3n(n + 2)$. If n is even then both n and $(n + 2)$
are divisible by 2, so $3n^2 + 6n$ will have factors of 3, 2 and 2
i.e. a factor of 12

27 Cosine rule

⊳G 1 $a^2 = b^2 + c^2 - 2bc \cos A$
$a^2 = 5^2 + 8^2 - 2 \times 5 \times 8 \cos 122° = 131.3935$
$a = 11.5\,\text{cm}$ (3 s.f.)

⊳G 2 $\cos B = \frac{a^2 + c^2 - b^2}{2ac}$
$= \frac{9^2 + 6^2 - 12^2}{2 \times 6 \times 9} = -\frac{1}{4}$
$B = \cos^{-1}(-0.25) = 104°$

3 437 m

4 17.4 km

28. Sine rule

G 1 $\angle ABC = 180 - 53 - 59 = 68°$

$$\frac{b}{\sin B} = \frac{c}{\sin C}$$

$$\frac{9}{\sin 68°} = \frac{c}{\sin 53°}$$

so $c = \dfrac{9 \sin 53°}{\sin 68°} = 8.32\,\text{cm}$ (3 s.f.)

G 2 (a) $\dfrac{\sin x}{14} = \dfrac{\sin 18°}{8}$

$\sin x = \dfrac{14 \sin 18°}{8} = 0.5408$ (3 d.p.)

(b) $x = \sin^{-1}(0.5408) = 32.7°$
or $x = 180° - (32.7°) = 147.3°$ (1 d.p.)

3 (a) 17.8 cm　　(b) 59.2°　　(c) 212 cm²

29. Trigonometric graphs

1 (a)

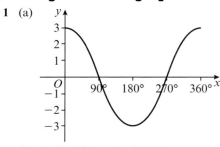

(b) $(0, 3)$, $(180°, -3)$, $(360°, 3)$

G 2

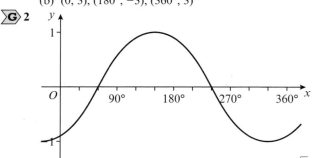

(b) When $x = 0$: $y = \sin(0 - 60°) = -\sin(60°) = -\dfrac{\sqrt{3}}{2}$

$\left(0, -\dfrac{\sqrt{3}}{2}\right)$

When $y = 0$: $0 = \sin(x - 60°)$,
so $x = 0 + 60° = 60°$
or $x = 180° + 60° = 240°$
$(60°, 0)$, $(240°, 0)$

3 $a = 1.5$, $b = 30°$

30. Trigonometric equations 1

G 1 $\sin x = \frac{2}{5} = 0.4$

$x = \sin^{-1}(0.4) = 23.6°$　or $x = 180° - 23.6° = 156.4°$

G 2 $\tan x = 3$

$x = \tan^{-1}(3) = 71.6°$
or $x = 180° + 71.6° = 251.6°$

3 (a)

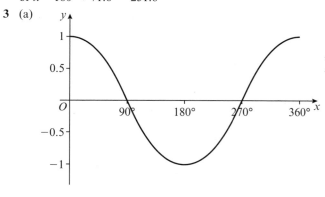

(b) $x = 101.5°$ or $258.5°$

4 (a) $x = -36.9°$ or $-143.1°$

(b) $x = -48.2°$ or $48.2°$

31. Trigonometric identities

G 1 (a) $3 \sin x = 2 \cos^2 x$

$\sin^2 x + \cos^2 x = 1$ so $\cos^2 x = 1 - \sin^2 x$

$3 \sin x = 2(1 - \sin^2 x)$

so $2 \sin^2 x + 3 \sin x - 2 = 0$

(b) $2 \sin^2 x + 3 \sin x - 2 = 0$

$(2 \sin x - 1)(\sin x + 2) = 0$

$\sin x = \frac{1}{2}$　$(\sin x \neq -2)$

$x = 30°$ or $x = 150°$

G 2 (a) $\dfrac{\sin \theta}{\cos \theta} = \frac{2}{3}$

$\tan \theta = \frac{2}{3}$

(b) $\theta = \tan^{-1}\left(\frac{2}{3}\right)$

$\theta = 33.7°$ or $\theta = 213.7°$

3 45°, 225°, 210° and 330°

4 60°, 113.6°, 246.4°, 300°

32. Trigonometric equations 2

G 1 (a) $0 \leqslant 2x \leqslant 360°$. Let $Z = 2x$

$Z = \sin^{-1}\left(\frac{1}{2}\right) = 30°$

or $Z = 180° - 30° = 150°$

$2x = 30°$ or $150°$

$x = 15°$ or $x = 75°$

(b) $-50° \leqslant x - 50° \leqslant 130°$. Let $Z = X - 50°$

$Z = \cos^{-1}(0.3) = 72.5°$

or $Z = 360° - 72.5° = 287.5°$ (outside range)

$x - 50° = 72.5°$

$x = 122.5°$

2 23.2°, $-156.8°$

3 $\theta = 38.6°$, 121.4°

4 18°, 138°, 198° and 318°

33. Vectors

G 1 (a) $\left|\overrightarrow{OP}\right| = \sqrt{1^2 + 7^2} = \sqrt{1 + 49} = \sqrt{50} = 5\sqrt{2}$

(b) $\overrightarrow{QP} = \overrightarrow{QO} + \overrightarrow{OP}$

$= \overrightarrow{OP} - \overrightarrow{OQ}$

$= \mathbf{i} + 7\mathbf{j} - (3\mathbf{i} + 2\mathbf{j})$

$= -2\mathbf{i} + 5\mathbf{j}$

(c) $\sqrt{29}$

2 (a) $\frac{1}{10}(8\mathbf{i} - 6\mathbf{j})$　　(b) $\frac{1}{17}(8\mathbf{i} + 15\mathbf{j})$　　(c) $\frac{1}{13}(12\mathbf{i} - 5\mathbf{j})$

3 (a) (i) $\overrightarrow{PQ} = -3\mathbf{i} - 5\mathbf{j}$　　(ii) $\left|\overrightarrow{PQ}\right| = \sqrt{34}$

(b) (i) $\overrightarrow{PQ} = -9\mathbf{i} - 13\mathbf{j}$　　(ii) $\left|\overrightarrow{PQ}\right| = \sqrt{250}$ or $5\sqrt{10}$

4 $\lambda = \pm \sqrt{20}$ or $\pm 2\sqrt{5}$

5 $\mu = -\frac{12}{5}$ and $\mu = 2$

34. Solving vector problems

G 1 (a) $\overrightarrow{AB} = \overrightarrow{AO} + \overrightarrow{OB} = \overrightarrow{OB} - \overrightarrow{OA} = \begin{pmatrix} 4 \\ 2 \end{pmatrix} - \begin{pmatrix} -2 \\ 5 \end{pmatrix} = \begin{pmatrix} 6 \\ -3 \end{pmatrix}$

$\overrightarrow{BC} = \overrightarrow{BO} + \overrightarrow{OC} = \overrightarrow{OC} - \overrightarrow{OB} = \begin{pmatrix} 6 \\ 4 \end{pmatrix} - \begin{pmatrix} 4 \\ 2 \end{pmatrix} = \begin{pmatrix} 2 \\ 2 \end{pmatrix}$

$\overrightarrow{AC} = \overrightarrow{AO} + \overrightarrow{OC} = \overrightarrow{OC} - \overrightarrow{OA} = \begin{pmatrix} 6 \\ 4 \end{pmatrix} - \begin{pmatrix} -2 \\ 5 \end{pmatrix} = \begin{pmatrix} 8 \\ -1 \end{pmatrix}$

(b) 9

(c) 18

(d) $\begin{pmatrix} 0 \\ 7 \end{pmatrix}$

2 (a) (i) $5\mathbf{b} - 4\mathbf{a}$ (ii) $\frac{5}{3}(2\mathbf{b} - \mathbf{a})$

(b) $\overrightarrow{PR} = 3(2\mathbf{b} - \mathbf{a})$ or $\overrightarrow{QR} = \frac{4}{3}(2\mathbf{b} - \mathbf{a})$

$\overrightarrow{PR}$, $\overrightarrow{QR}$ and $\overrightarrow{PQ}$ are multiples of $(2\mathbf{b} - \mathbf{a})$ and have a common point, so P, Q and R are collinear.

35. Differentiating from first principles

G 1 $f'(x) = \lim_{h \to 0} \dfrac{f(x + h) - f(x)}{h}$

$= \lim_{h \to 0} \dfrac{(x + h)^3 + 5(x + h)^2 - x^3 - 5x^2}{h}$

$= \lim_{h \to 0} \dfrac{x^3 + 3x^2h + 3xh^2 + h^3 + 5x^2 + 10xh + 5h^2 - x^3 - 5x^2}{h}$

$= \lim_{h \to 0} \dfrac{3x^2h + 3xh^2 + h^3 + 10xh + 5h^2}{h}$

$= \lim_{h \to 0} (3x^2 + 3xh + h^2 + 10x + 5h)$

As $h \to 0$, $3xh \to 0$, $h^2 \to 0$ and $5h \to 0$,

so $f'(x) = 3x^2 + 10x$ as required.

2 $f'(3) = \lim_{h \to 0} \dfrac{f(3 + h) - f(3)}{h}$

$= \lim_{h \to 0} \dfrac{2(3 + h)^2 - 7(3 + h) + 1 - [2(3)^2 - 7(3) + 1]}{h}$

$= \lim_{h \to 0} \dfrac{18 + 12h + 2h^2 - 21 - 7h + 1 - 18 + 21 - 1}{h}$

$= \lim_{h \to 0} \dfrac{5h + 2h^2}{h} = \lim_{h \to 0} (5 + 2h)$

As $h \to 0$, $2h \to 0$ so $f'(3) = 5$

3 $f(x) = ax^2 + 3bx$

$f'(x) = \lim_{h \to 0} \dfrac{f(x + h) - f(x)}{h}$

$= \lim_{h \to 0} \dfrac{a(x + h)^2 + 3b(x + h) - ax^2 - 3bx}{h}$

$= \lim_{h \to 0} \dfrac{ax^2 + 2ahx + ah^2 + 3bx + 3bh - ax^2 - 3bx}{h}$

$= \lim_{h \to 0} (2ax + ah + 3b)$

$= 2ax + 3b$

36. Differentiation 1

1 $5 - \frac{9}{2}x^{\frac{1}{2}} + 12x^2$

G 2 $y = 5x^2 + 2x^{-1} - 3x^{-2}$

$\dfrac{dy}{dx} = 10x - 2x^{-2} + 6x^{-3}$

G 3 $f(x) = \dfrac{3x - 2\sqrt{x}}{x} = \dfrac{3x}{x} - \dfrac{2\sqrt{x}}{x} = 3 - 2x^{-\frac{1}{2}}$

$f'(x) = x^{-\frac{3}{2}}$

4 (a) $5x^{-\frac{2}{3}} - 2x^{-1}$

(b) $\dfrac{dy}{dx} = 4 - \frac{10}{3}x^{-\frac{5}{3}} + 2x^{-2}$

5 $f'(x) = -16x^{-2} - 4x^{-\frac{3}{2}}$

37. Differentiation 2

1 (a) $\dfrac{dy}{dx} = 12x^2 - 3$

(b) $\dfrac{d^2y}{dx^2} = 24x$

G 2 (a) When $x = 1$, $y = 5 \times 1 - \dfrac{2}{1^2} = 5 - 2 = 3$, so P lies on C

(b) $y = 5x - \dfrac{2}{x^2} = 5x - 2x^{-2}$

$\dfrac{dy}{dx} = 5 + 4x^{-3} = 5 + \dfrac{4}{x^3}$

When $x = 1$, $\dfrac{dy}{dx} = 5 + \dfrac{4}{1^3} = 9$

Gradient at $P = 9$

3 (a) $f'(x) = 3 + 4x^{-2}$ (b) $x = \pm\frac{2}{3}$

4 (a)

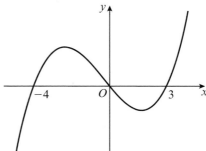

(b) $3x^2 + 2x - 12$

(c) At $x = -4$, gradient $= 28$

At $x = 0$, gradient $= -12$

At $x = 3$, gradient $= 21$

38. Tangents and normals

G 1 $y = \frac{1}{3}x^3 + 2x^2 - 8x + 4$

$\dfrac{dy}{dx} = x^2 + 4x - 8$

When $x = 3$, $\dfrac{dy}{dx} = 3^2 + 4 \times 3 - 8 = 13$

Equation of tangent: $y - 7 = 13(x - 3)$ giving $y = 13x - 32$

G 2 (a) $y = 8 \times 4 + 2 \times 4^{\frac{3}{2}} - 3 \times 4^2 = 32 + 16 - 48 = 0$,

so $P\,(4, 0)$ lies on C

(b) $\dfrac{dy}{dx} = 8 + 3x^{\frac{1}{2}} - 6x$

(c) $\dfrac{dy}{dx} = 8 + 3x^{\frac{1}{2}} - 6x$

When $x = 4$, $\dfrac{dy}{dx} = 8 + 6 - 24 = -10$

Gradient of tangent $= -\frac{10}{1}$ so gradient of normal $= \frac{1}{10}$

Equation of normal: $y - 0 = \frac{1}{10}(x - 4)$

giving $x - 10y - 4 = 0$

3 (a) $y = x^3 + 2x^2 - 9x - 18$

$\dfrac{dy}{dx} = 3x^2 + 4x - 9$

(b) When $x = -3$, $\dfrac{dy}{dx} = 6$

$y - 0 = 6(x + 3)$

$y = 6x + 18$

(c) $3x^2 + 4x - 9 = 6$

$3x^2 + 4x - 15 = 0$

$(x + 3)(3x - 5) = 0$

$x = \frac{5}{3}$

39. Stationary points 1

G 1 $\dfrac{dy}{dx} = 6x - 18$

$6x - 18 = 0$

$x = 3 \Rightarrow y = -27$

Coordinates are $(3, -27)$

G 2 $\dfrac{dy}{dx} = -5 + 40x^{-3} = -5 + \dfrac{40}{x^3}$

If $x > 2$, then $x^3 > 8$, and $\dfrac{40}{x^3} < 5$

$\dfrac{40}{x^3} - 5 < 0$

So $\dfrac{dy}{dx} < 0$ and hence y is decreasing.

3 $(2, -3)$

4 $\left(-\frac{1}{3}, \frac{185}{27}\right)$ and $(5, -69)$

5 $k = -\frac{2}{3}$

40. Stationary points 2

1 (a) $\frac{dy}{dx} = 3x^2 + 6x - 24$, $\frac{dy}{dx} = 0$ when $3x^2 + 6x - 24 = 0$

$3(x^2 + 2x - 8) = 0$, $3(x + 4)(x - 2) = 0$,

$x = -4$ and $x = 2$

When $x = -4$, $y = 80$, and when $x = 2$, $y = -28$

(b) $\frac{d^2 y}{dx^2} = 6x + 6$

When $x = -4$, $\frac{d^2 y}{dx^2} = -18$, so we have a maximum

When $x = 2$, $\frac{d^2 y}{dx^2} = 18$, so we have a minimum

2 (a) $x = \sqrt{3}$ or $-\sqrt{3}$

(b) $\frac{d^2 y}{dx^2} = -72x^{-5}$

At P $x = \sqrt{3}$ $\frac{d^2 y}{dx^2} = -\frac{8\sqrt{3}}{3} < 0$ so maximum

At Q $x = -\sqrt{3}$, $\frac{d^2 y}{dx^2} = \frac{8\sqrt{3}}{3} > 0$ so minimum

3 (a) (b)

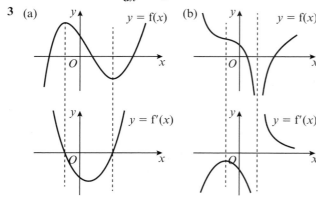

41. Modelling with calculus

1 (a) Volume $= 2x^2 y = 8000$

$y = \frac{8000}{2x^2} = \frac{4000}{x^2}$

$A = 2xy + 4xy + 2x^2 = 6xy + 2x^2 = 6x\left(\frac{4000}{x^2}\right) + 2x^2$

$= \frac{24\,000}{x} + 2x^2$

(b) $A = 24\,000x^{-1} + 2x^2$

$\frac{dA}{dx} -24\,000x^{-2} + 4x = 0$ for a stationary point

$4x = 24\,000x^{-2}$

$4x^3 = 24\,000$

$x^3 = 6000$

$x = 18.2$ cm

(c) $\frac{d^2 A}{dx^2} = 48\,000x^{-3} + 4 = \frac{48\,000}{x^3} + 4 = \frac{48\,000}{6000} + 4 = 12 > 0$

so minimum

(d) Minimum amount of cardboard $= \frac{24\,000}{18.2} + 2(18.2)^2$

$= 1981.2$ cm^2

2 (a) $V = \pi r^2 h$

$A = 2\pi r^2 + 2\pi rh = 900$

$2\pi rh = 900 - 2\pi r^2$

$h = \frac{450}{\pi r} - r$

$V = \pi r^2 \left(\frac{450}{\pi r} - r\right) = 450r - \pi r^3$

(b) $V = 2073$ cm^3

(c) $r = 6.9$ cm

$\frac{d^2 V}{dr^2} = -6\pi r = -130 < 0$ so maximum

42. Integration

1 $y = 4x - 3x^{-2}$

$\int y\, dx = \frac{4x^2}{2} - \frac{3x^{-1}}{-1} + c = 2x^2 + \frac{3}{x} + c$

2 $\int(3x^2 - 5 + x^{-\frac{1}{2}})\, dx = \frac{3x^3}{3} - 5x + 2x^{\frac{1}{2}} + c$

$= x^3 - 5x + 2x^{\frac{1}{2}} + c$

3 $-3x^{-1} + \frac{3x^{-2}}{4} + c$

4 (a) $(3 - 2\sqrt{x})^2 = (3 - 2\sqrt{x})(3 - 2\sqrt{x}) = 9 - 12\sqrt{x} + 4x$,

$k = 12$

(b) $9x - 8x^{\frac{3}{2}} + 2x^2 + c$

5 (a) $p = \frac{3}{2}$, $q = 2$

(b) $\frac{8x^{\frac{5}{2}}}{5} - \frac{2x^3}{3} + c$

43. Finding the constant

1 (a) $f(x) = \int\left(3x + \frac{2}{x^2}\right) dx$

$= \int(3x + 2x^{-2})\, dx$

$= \frac{3x^2}{2} - 2x^{-1} + c = \frac{3x^2}{2} - \frac{2}{x} + c$

$10 = \frac{3 \times 4}{2} - \frac{2}{2} + c$

$c = 5$

$f(x) = \frac{3x^2}{2} - \frac{2}{x} + 5$

(b) $f(x) = \frac{3x^2}{2} - \frac{2}{x} + 5$

$f(-1) = \frac{3}{2} + 2 + 5 = 8.5$

2 $\frac{dy}{dx} = \frac{x - 3}{\sqrt{x}} = x^{\frac{1}{2}} - 3x^{-\frac{1}{2}}$

$y = \int\left(x^{\frac{1}{2}} - 3x^{-\frac{1}{2}}\right) dx = \frac{2x^{\frac{3}{2}}}{3} - 6x^{\frac{1}{2}} + c$

$\frac{1}{3} = \frac{2 \times 8}{3} - 6 \times 2 + c = \frac{16}{3} - 12 + c$

$c = 7$

$y = \frac{2x^{\frac{3}{2}}}{3} - 6x^{\frac{1}{2}} + 7$

3 (a) $\frac{dy}{dx} = \frac{(x^2 - 2)^2}{x^2} = \frac{(x^2 - 2)(x^2 - 2)}{x^2} = \frac{x^4 - 4x^2 + 4}{x^2}$

$\frac{dy}{dx} = x^2 - 4 + 4x^{-2}$

(b) $y = \frac{x^3}{3} - 4x - 4x^{-1} + 5$

44. Definite integration

1 $\int_1^2 (x^3 - 3x^2 + 5x - 7)\, dx = \left[\frac{x^4}{4} - x^3 + \frac{5x^2}{2} - 7x\right]_1^2$

$= (4 - 8 + 10 - 14) - \left(\frac{1}{4} - 1 + \frac{5}{2} - 7\right) = -8 - \left(-\frac{21}{4}\right) = -\frac{11}{4}$

2 $\int_1^2\left(2x^2 + 3 - \frac{5}{x^2}\right) dx = \int_1^2(2x^2 + 3 - 5x^{-2})\, dx$

$= \left[\frac{2x^3}{3} + 3x + 5x^{-1}\right]_1^2 = \left[\frac{2x^3}{3} + 3x + \frac{5}{x}\right]_1^2$

$= \left(\frac{16}{3} + 6 + \frac{5}{2}\right) - \left(\frac{2}{3} + 3 + 5\right) = \frac{83}{6} - \frac{26}{3} = \frac{31}{6}$

3 $\frac{47}{2}$

4 $30 + 4\sqrt{2}$

5 $\frac{41}{8}$

45. Area under a curve

1 Graph crosses the x-axis at $x = -1$ and $x = 3$

$y = 3 + 2x - x^2$

$\int_{-1}^3 (3 + 2x - x^2)\, dx = \left[3x + \frac{2x^2}{2} - \frac{x^3}{3}\right]_{-1}^3 = \left[3x + x^2 - \frac{x^3}{3}\right]_{-1}^3$

$= (9 + 9 - 9) - \left(-3 + 1 + \frac{1}{3}\right) = 9 - \left(-\frac{5}{3}\right) = \frac{32}{3}$

Area $= \frac{32}{3}$

G 2 Graph crosses the x-axis at $x = -2$ and $x = 4$
$y = x^2 - 2x - 8$
$\int_{-2}^{4}(x^2 - 2x - 8)\,dx = \left[\frac{x^3}{3} - \frac{2x^2}{2} - 8x\right]_{-2}^{4} = \left[\frac{x^3}{3} - x^2 - 8x\right]_{-2}^{4}$
$= \left(\frac{64}{3} - 16 - 32\right) - \left(-\frac{8}{3} - 4 + 16\right) = -\frac{80}{3} - \frac{28}{3} = -36$
Area = 36

3 24

46. More areas

G 1 $L\,(2, 0)$; $M\,(4, 0)$ At N: $x = 6$, $y = 6^2 - 6 \times 6 + 8 = 8$
Area of triangle = $\frac{1}{2} \times$ base $\times$ height $= \frac{1}{2} \times 4 \times 8 = 16$
$\int_{4}^{6}(x^2 - 6x + 8)\,dx = \left[\frac{x^3}{3} - \frac{6x^2}{2} + 8x\right]_{4}^{6} = \left[\frac{x^3}{3} - 3x^2 + 8x\right]_{4}^{6}$
$= (72 - 108 + 48) - \left(\frac{64}{3} - 48 + 32\right)$
$= 12 - \frac{16}{3} = \frac{20}{3}$
Area of $R = 16 - \frac{20}{3} = \frac{28}{3}$

2 (a) $A\,(-6, 38)$, $B\,(1, 17)$ (b) Area of $S = \frac{385}{2} - 135\frac{1}{3} = \frac{343}{6}$

47. Exponential functions

1 (a) D   (b) C   (c) A   (d) B

G 2 (b)   (c)

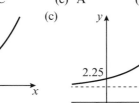

(d)

3 (a) $6e^{6x}$ (b) $-3e^{-3x}$ (c) $2e^{\frac{x}{2}}$
(d) $1.2e^{0.2x}$ (e) $-7e^{-x} + 8e^{-4x}$ (f) $9e^{3x} + 2e^{-2x}$
(g) $\frac{5}{4}e^{\frac{5x}{4}} + \frac{9}{2}e^{\frac{9x}{4}}$

48. Logarithms

G 1 (a) $8^2 = 64$ so $\log_8 64 = 2$
(b) $3\log_a 2 = \log_a 2^3 = \log_a 8$
$\log_a 8 + \log_a 7 = \log_a(8 \times 7) = \log_a 56$

2 (a) $p = \frac{1}{16}$ (b) $y = 5$

3 (a) $\log_a 200$ (b) $\log_a \frac{27}{4}$

G 4 $\log_4 y = \log_4 4x^3$
$= \log_4 4 + \log_4 x^3$
$= 1 + 3\log_4 x$

5 $y^2 = 9x^4$
$\log_3 y^2 = \log_3 9x^4$
$2\log_3 y = \log_3 9 + \log_3 x^4$
$2\log_3 y = \log_3 3^2 + 4\log_3 x$
$2\log_3 y = 2\log_3 3 + 4\log_3 x$
$2\log_3 y = 2 + 4\log_3 x$
$\log_3 y = 1 + 2\log_3 x$

6 $3\log_a x + \frac{1}{2}\log_a y - 4\log_a z$

49. Equations with logs

G 1 $\log_3 \frac{2x - 1}{x} = 1$
$\frac{2x - 1}{x} = 3^1$
$2x - 1 = 3x$
$x = -1$

2 $x = \frac{1}{2}$

G 3 $a = 4b$ ①
$\log_2 a + \log_2 b = 3$ ②
$\log_2 4b + \log_2 b = 3$
$\log_2 4b^2 = 3$
$4b^2 = 2^3$
$4b^2 = 8$
$b^2 = 2$
$b = \sqrt{2}$ and $a = 4\sqrt{2}$ (a and b both positive)

4 (a) $2\log_2(x - 2) - \log_2(6 - x) = 1$
$\log_2 \frac{(x - 2)^2}{(6 - x)} = 1$
$\frac{(x - 2)^2}{(6 - x)} = 2^1$
$x^2 - 4x + 4 = 2(6 - x)$
$x^2 - 2x - 8 = 0$
(b) $x = 4$ $(x \neq -2)$

5 $x = 27$ or $\frac{1}{27}$

50. Exponential equations

G 1 (a) $3^x = 5$
$\log 3^x = \log 5$
$x\log 3 = \log 5$
$x = \frac{\log 5}{\log 3} = 1.46$
(b) Let $Y = 3^x$ so $3^{2x} = (3^x)^2 = Y^2$
$Y^2 - 8Y + 15 = 0$
$(Y - 3)(Y - 5) = 0$
$Y = 3$ or 5, so $3^x = 3$ or $3^x = 5$
$x = 1$ or $x = \frac{\log 5}{\log 3} = 1.46$

2 $x = 0.43$

3 $x = 0$, $x = 0.936$

4 (a) 7.638   (b) 1.723

5 The quadratic is $0.5\log 3x^2 - \log 9x + \log 9 = 0$
Discriminant $= (\log 9)^2 - 4 \times 0.5\log 3 \times \log 9$
$= (\log 9)^2 - 2\log 3 \times \log 9$
$= (\log 9)^2 - \log 3^2 \times \log 9$
$= (\log 9)^2 - (\log 9)^2$
$= 0$ so the curves just touch

51. Natural logarithms

G 1 $\ln(5x + 24) = \ln(x + 2)^2$
$5x + 24 = (x + 2)^2$
$5x + 24 = x^2 + 4x + 4$
$0 = x^2 - x - 20$
$0 = (x - 5)(x + 4)$
$x = 5$
($x = -4$ is inadmissible since $\ln x$ is only defined for $x > 0$)

2 $x = 9$
($x = -2$ is inadmissible since $\ln x$ is only defined for $x > 0$)

3 $x = 0$, $x = \ln 2$

4 $x = \frac{\ln 5 + 1}{\ln 3 + 2}$

5 (a) $\frac{5x^2 - 13x - 6}{x^2 - 9} = \frac{(5x + 2)(x - 3)}{(x - 3)(x + 3)} = \frac{5x + 2}{x + 3}$
(b) $x = \frac{3e^2 - 2}{5 - e^2}$

52. Exponential modelling

G 1 (a) $370\,^{\circ}\mathrm{C}$
(b) $280 = 350e^{-0.08t} + 20$
$\frac{260}{350} = e^{-0.08t}$ so $\ln\left(\frac{260}{350}\right) = -0.08t$
$t = 3.72$ minutes (3 s.f.)

(c) 1.14 °C/min

(d) $e^{-0.08t} > 0$ for all values of t and $e^{-0.08t} \to 0$ as $t \to \infty$
So $T > 20$, i.e. the temperature can never fall to 18 °C

2 (a) 60 g

(b) $k = 0.00788$ (3 s.f.)

(c) 23.3 g (3 s.f.)

(d) 0.319 g/yr

(e)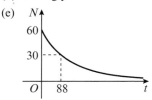

53. Modelling with logs

G 1 (a) $\log_{10} P = \log_{10}(at^n) = \log_{10} a + \log_{10} t^n = \log_{10} a + n\log_{10} t.$

(b) Intercept $= \log_{10} a$

(c) $n = \text{gradient} = \dfrac{1.67 - 1.48}{0.8} = 0.2375$
Intercept $= 1.48 = \log_{10} a$, so $a = 30.2$
So the equation is $P = 30.2\, t^{0.2375}$

(d) 66.6%

2 (a) $\log_{10} y = \log_{10} k + t\log_{10} b$ (b) $\log_{10} k$

(c) $y = 288(1.16)^t$ (d) £288 million

(e) 5.5 years

54. You are the examiner!

1 L is $y = -\frac{1}{2}x + \frac{5}{2}$ so gradient of line perpendicular to L is 2
Equation is $y - 4 = 2(x + 1)$
$\Rightarrow y - 4 = 2x + 2 \Rightarrow 2x - y + 6 = 0$

2 $y = 3x^2 - 2x + 4x^{-1}$ so $\dfrac{dy}{dx} = 6x - 2 - \dfrac{4}{x^2}$
When $x = 2$, $y = 12 - 4 + 2 = 10$ and $\dfrac{dy}{dx} = 12 - 2 - 1 = 9$
Equation of tangent is $y - 10 = 9(x - 2)$
$\Rightarrow y - 10 = 9x - 18 \Rightarrow y = 9x - 8$

3 From 1st equation, $y = 2x - 9$
Substituting for y in the 2nd equation gives $x^2 - x(2x - 9) = 20$
$x^2 - 2x^2 + 9x = 20 \Rightarrow x^2 - 9x + 20 = 0$
$\Rightarrow (x - 4)(x - 5) = 0 \Rightarrow x = 4$ and $x = 5$
When $x = 4$, $y = -1$ and when $x = 5$, $y = 1$

4 Range for $(x + 40°)$ is
$40° \leqslant (x + 40°) \leqslant 400°$
$\cos^{-1}(0.85) = 31.8°$ (1 d.p.),
which is not in the range
for $(x + 40°)$
$(x + 40°) = 360° - 31.8°$
or $360 + 31.8°$
$(x + 40°) = 328.2°$ or $391.8°$
$x = 288.2°$ or $351.8°$

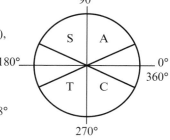

55. You are the examiner!

5 (a) $2e^{3x} - 9e^{2x} + 10e^x = 0$
$\Rightarrow e^x(2e^{2x} - 9e^x + 10) = 0 \Rightarrow e^x[2(e^x)^2 - 9e^x + 10] = 0$
$e^x(2e^x - 5)(e^x - 2) = 0$ so $e^x = 0$ (which is not possible)
or $e^x = 2$ or $e^x = \frac{5}{2}$
so $x = \ln 2$ or $x = \ln \frac{5}{2}$

(b) $\ln(4^x e^{3x + 2}) = \ln 5 \Rightarrow \ln 4^x + \ln e^{3x + 2} = \ln 5$
$x\ln 4 + (3x + 2)\ln e = \ln 5$
$\Rightarrow x\ln 4 + (3x + 2) = \ln 5$ (since $\ln e = 1$)
$x(\ln 4 + 3) = \ln 5 - 2$, so $x = \dfrac{\ln 5 - 2}{\ln 4 + 3}$

6 (a) $x^2 - 3x + 4 = 10 - 2x$
$x^2 - x - 6 = 0$
$(x + 2)(x - 3) = 0$
$x = -2$ or $x = 3$
When $x = -2$, $y = 14$, so A is $(-2, 14)$
and when $x = 3$, $y = 4$, so B is $(3, 4)$

(b) Area of trapezium formed by straight line and x-axis
between $x = -2$ and $x = 3$ is
$\frac{1}{2} \times 5 \times (14 + 4) = 45$
Area under curve between $x = -2$ and $x = 3$ is
$\int_{-2}^{3}(x^2 - 3x + 4)dx = \left[\dfrac{x^3}{3} - \dfrac{3x^2}{2} + 4x\right]_{-2}^{3}$
$= \left(9 - \frac{27}{2} + 12\right) - \left(-\frac{8}{3} - 6 - 8\right)$
$= 7\frac{1}{2} + 16\frac{2}{3} = 24\frac{1}{6}$
Shaded area $S = 45 - 24\frac{1}{6} = 20\frac{5}{6}$

STATISTICS

56. Sampling

1 (a) Systematic sampling

(b) Adds a degree of system or process and is easy to operate; ensures the sample is evenly distributed across the population

G 2 Sampling fraction $= \frac{65}{450}$
Number in sample playing football $= \frac{65}{450} \times 97 = 14$
Number in sample playing:
Tennis = 10; Rugby = 22; Squash = 19

3

Age (years)	16–24	25–44	45–64	65+
Number of members	96	171 to 177*	201 to 207*	110
Number in sample	16	29	34	18

* Total of these two cells must be 376

57. Mean

1 (a) 93.4 g (1 d.p.)   (b) 94.2 g (1 d.p.)

G 2 (a) The midpoint of the 6–12 minutes group is 9 minutes.
The midpoint of the 13–20 minutes group is 16.5 minutes.

(b) $\bar{x} = \dfrac{\Sigma fx}{\Sigma f} = \dfrac{6 \times 3 + 11 \times 9 + 7 \times 16.5 + 8 \times 25.5}{32}$
$= \dfrac{436.5}{32} = 13.6$ minutes (1 d.p.)

3 14.2 km (1 d.p.)

58. Median and quartiles

G 1 (a) 28

(b) $n = 23$, $\frac{n}{2} = 11.5 \Rightarrow$ 12th value, so median $Q_2 = 23$
$\frac{n}{4} = 5.75 \Rightarrow$ 6th value, so $Q_1 = 14$;
$\frac{3n}{4} = 17.25 \Rightarrow$ 18th value, so $Q_3 = 32$

2 Modal age = 25, median = 41, IQR = $52 - 29 = 23$

3 Median = 71, IQR = $73 - 70 = 3$

59. Linear interpolation

G 1 $\frac{n}{2} = 135$, so the median is $(135 - 29) = 106$ values into the $10 \leqslant w < 15$ group.
This group is 5 kg wide so each member is worth $\frac{5}{121}$ kg.
$Q_2 = 10 + 106 \times \frac{5}{121}$ kg $= 14.380\,16... = 14.4$ kg (1 d.p.)

2 (a) $Q_1 = 26.6$ mph, $Q_2 = 37.1$ mph, $Q_3 = 47.9$ mph

(b) 20% of vehicles exceed 51.66 mph. The claim is justified because more than 20% exceed 50 mph.

3 $Q_1 = 17$ mm, $Q_2 = 32$ mm, $Q_3 = 49.9$ mm (1 d.p.)

60. Standard deviation 1

 1

Mark	Frequency (f)	Midpoint (x)	$f \times x$
$0 < x \leqslant 10$	16	5	80
$10 < x \leqslant 30$	32	20	640
$30 < x \leqslant 50$	38	40	1520
$50 < x \leqslant 60$	24	55	1320
$60 < x \leqslant 80$	10	70	700

Mean = 35.5 marks, SD = 19.2 marks

2 Mean = 37.1 years, SD = 14.9 years

3 Mean = 34.8 cm, SD = 11.6 cm

4 Mean = 23.1 letters, SD = 6.24 letters

61. Standard deviation 2

 1 $\Sigma f = 160$

$\Sigma fx = 12 \times 5 + 27 \times 12.5 + 85 \times 22.5 + 36 \times 40 = 3750$

$\Sigma fx^2 = 12 \times 5^2 + 27 \times 12.5^2 + 85 \times 22.5^2 + 36 \times 40^2$
$= 105\,150$

Variance $= \dfrac{105\,150}{160} - \left(\dfrac{3750}{160}\right)^2 = 107.871...$

Standard deviation $= \sqrt{107.871...} = 10.386...$
$= 10.4$ minutes (3 s.f.)

2 £0.873 million (3 s.f.)

3 (a) 38 mm and 70.5 mm   (b) 25.2 mm (3 s.f.)

62. Coding

 1

Yield, w (kg)	Frequency (f)	Midpoint (w)	u ($w - 80$)	$f \times u$	u^2	$f \times u^2$
$65 \leqslant w < 75$	21	70	-10	-210	100	2100
$75 \leqslant w < 85$	18	80	0	0	0	0
$85 \leqslant w < 105$	11	95	15	165	225	2475
$105 \leqslant w < 125$	7	115	35	245	1225	8575
			Total	**200**		**13150**

Mean for $u = \dfrac{\Sigma fu}{n} = \dfrac{200}{57} = 3.508$, so mean for

$w = 3.508 + 80 = 83.5$ kg (3 s.f.)

Variance for $u = \dfrac{\Sigma fu^2}{n} - \left[\dfrac{\Sigma fu}{n^2}\right] = \dfrac{13\,150}{57} - (3.5)^2 = 218.45$

Standard deviation for $u = \sqrt{218.45} = 14.78$, so standard deviation for $w = 14.8$ kg (3 s.f.)

2 Mean = 25.3, SD = 8.96

3 (a) Mean = 117.9, SD = 9.20
(b) Mean = 120.6, SD = 9.66

63. Box plots and outliers

 1 IQR = 40 − 28 = 12
$1.25 \times$ IQR $= 1.25 \times 12 = 15$
$Q_3 + 15 = 40 + 15 = 55$
$Q_1 - 15 = 28 - 15 = 13$

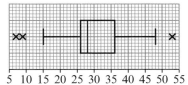

2 (a) (i) 28   (ii) Lower quartile

(b) IQR = 36 − 28 = 8, 28 − 1.5 × 8 = 28 − 12 = 16;
10 is less than this value so it is an outlier.

3

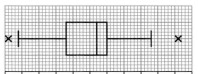

IQR = 10 $Q_3 + 15 = 36 + 15 = 51$ $Q_1 - 15 = 26 - 15 = 11$
Outliers at 7, 9 and 53

64. Cumulative frequency diagrams

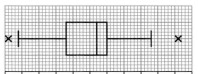 **1** (a)

Length, l (mm)	Number of insects	Cumulative frequency
$0 < l \leqslant 5$	65	65
$5 < l \leqslant 10$	50	115
$10 < l \leqslant 20$	60	175
$20 < l \leqslant 30$	25	200
$30 < l \leqslant 40$	15	215
$40 < l \leqslant 50$	10	225

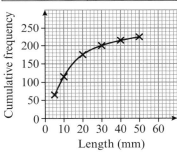

(b) 20th percentile $= \frac{20}{100} \times 225 = $ 45th value
80th percentile $= \frac{80}{100} \times 225 = $ 180th value
Interpercentile range = 21 − 3 = 18 mm

2 (a)

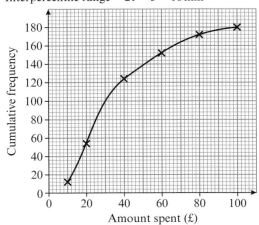

(b) Median = £29, IQR = 46 − 18 = £28

(c) 12 people   (d) 70 − 12 = £58

Answers

65. Histograms

1 Frequency for $0 < t \le 10$ class = $2.8 \times 10 = 28$
Frequency for $10 < t \le 30$ class = $2 \times 20 = 40$

Time, t (minutes)	Number of cars
$0 < t \le 10$	28
$10 < t \le 30$	40
$30 < t \le 60$	48
$60 < t \le 80$	16

2 (a) Frequency density (height of bar) for $20 < v \le 30$ is 11
The frequency for the $45 < v \le 50$ group is 110

  (b) 335 cars

3 Width = 2 cm, height = 1.5 cm

66. Comparing distributions

1 The median for the boys' marks (52) is less than the median for the girls' marks (60), so the boys did less well overall.

The IQR for the boys was 20 compared with 30 for the girls so the boys' marks were more closely grouped than the girls' marks.

Only 25% of the boys scored more than 58, whereas 50% of the girls scored more than 60.

2 (a) Mean = 36.3, SD = 9.67

  (b) Class PX has a higher mean, so, on average, the students in PX scored better than those in class HY.
The standard deviation for class HY was lower than for PX, meaning that the results for HY were more closely grouped together.
In addition, the mean for PX was lower than the median but for HY the mean was higher than the median, which means that the results for PX were grouped towards the top end of the mark range but for HY the results were grouped slightly towards the lower end of the mark range.

67. Correlation and cleaning data

1 (a) IQR = $72.5 - 67.5 = 5$, $3 \times$ IQR = 15, $71.5 - 15 = 56.5$, which is greater than 15.

  (b) To weigh 55 kg (approx 8.5 stone) and be 173 cm (approx 5′ 8″) tall isn't particularly unusual, so the data item could easily have been retained, but since 55 is an outlier there is some justification.

  (c)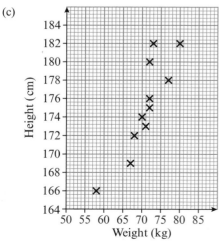

  (d) The scatter diagram shows the 11 results to have good positive correlation which means that an increase in weight is usually accompanied by an increase in height.

2 (a) $Q_1 = 29$, $Q_2 = 33$ and $Q_3 = 39$

  (b) $Q_2 + 3 \times$ IQR = $33 + 3 \times 10 = 63$, so 70 is an outlier.

  (c) A person of 70 is still likely to have a good short-term memory, so valid to retain this result.

68. Regression

1 (a) The gradient is 2.11, so every year the average CO_2 level increases by just over 2 parts per million.

  (b) There is strong positive correlation so a linear model is suitable.

2 (a) For every °C rise in temperature the energy consumption falls by 2.25 kWh.

  (b) 25.7 kWh is the energy consumption when the temperature is 0°C

  (c) Strong negative correlation, so a linear model is suitable.

69. Using regression lines

1 (a) Reading off values of the independent variable within the range of the given data. This is reliable.

  (b) Estimating a value of the dependent variable outside the range of the given data. This is much less reliable.

2 (a) (i) 2005 is 14 years after 1991. The regression equation will give a reliable estimate of CO_2 since 14 is within the range 1 to 22 (interpolation).

    (ii) 2016 is 25 years after 1991. This is not covered by the scale on the x-axis. The estimate will be unreliable (extrapolation).

  (b) CO_2 (y) is the dependent variable. The regression equation cannot be used to predict the value of the date (x), the independent variable.

3 (a) (i) The answer is reliable because 14 °C is within the range of the given data (interpolation).

    (ii) kWh (y) is the dependent variable. The regression equation cannot be used to predict the average temperature (x), the independent variable.

  (b) When $x = 12$, the equation would give -1.3 kWh of energy, which is a negative quantity and clearly not possible. The household will always use some energy for heating, lighting and other electrical appliances. The regression equation only covers temperatures up to approximately 5 °C, so attempting to use it for $x = 12$ is unreliable (extrapolation) because this is outside the range of the given data.

70. Drawing Venn diagrams

1 (a) The 11 children who had a cat and a dog include the 2 children who had all three pets.

So $11 - 2 = 9$ children had a cat and a dog but not a rabbit. This is C and D but not R.

The 7 children who had a cat and a rabbit include the 2 children who had all three pets.

So $7 - 2 = 5$ children had a cat and a rabbit but not a dog. This is C and R but not D.

Similarly, $5 - 2 = 3$ is the number for the region D and R but not C.

The total number who had a cat is 31, but $9 + 5 + 2 = 16$ of these have already been counted, leaving $31 - 16 = 15$ as the number in the 'cat only' region.

Similarly 'dog only' = $35 - (9 + 3 + 2) = 21$, and 'rabbit only' = $18 - (5 + 3 + 2) = 8$.

The final calculation is to add up all the numbers found so far and subtract from 80 to find out how many children had none of these three pets.
$80 - (15 + 21 + 8 + 9 + 5 + 3 + 2) = 17$

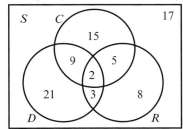

(b) Children who did not have a cat or a dog = 25

2 (a)

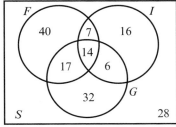

(b) The number who had been to exactly two of the three countries = $17 + 7 + 6 = 30$

71. Using Venn diagrams

1 (a) The total number of students =
$21 + 4 + 12 + 6 + 15 + 22 = 80$
The number taking only one subject =
$21 + 12 + 15 = 48$
So the probability is $\frac{48}{80} = \frac{3 \times 16}{5 \times 16} = \frac{3}{5}$

(b) The number of students taking maths or English or both = $21 + 4 + 12 + 6 = 43$
So probability = $\frac{43}{80}$

2 (a)

(b) 52%

3 (a)

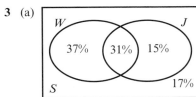

(b) P(W or J but not both) = $0.37 + 0.15 = 0.52$

72. Independent events

1 (a) $q + r$ (b) $q + r - qr$

2 Total number of people = $7 + 4 + 9 + 2 + 3 + 2 + 5 + 8 = 40$
$P(C) = \frac{7 + 4 + 2 + 3}{40} = \frac{16}{40} = \frac{2}{5}$
$P(G) = \frac{5 + 2 + 2 + 3}{40} = \frac{12}{40} = \frac{3}{10}$
$P(C \text{ and } G) = \frac{2 + 3}{40} = \frac{5}{40} = \frac{1}{8}$
$P(C) \times P(G) = \frac{2}{5} \times \frac{3}{10} = \frac{6}{50} = \frac{3}{25}$
$\frac{1}{8} \neq \frac{3}{25}$ so the events are not independent

3 (a) $\frac{17}{25}$ (b) $\frac{51}{200}$

73. Tree diagrams

1 (a)

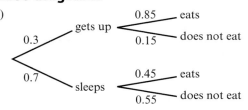

(b) P(does not eat) = $0.3 \times 0.15 + 0.7 \times 0.55$
$= 0.045 + 0.385 = 0.43$

(c) $3 \times (0.43)^2 \times 0.57 = 0.316\,179$

2 (a)

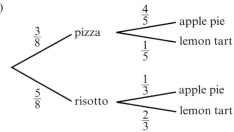

(b) P(Keisha eats either risotto or lemon tart, but not both) = $\frac{17}{60}$

(c) $\frac{25}{144}$

74. Random variables

1 (a) $P(X = 1) = k \times 1^2 = k$ $P(X = 2) = k \times 2^2 = 4k$
$P(X = 3) = k \times 3^2 = 9k$ $P(X = 4) = 3 \times k \times 4 = 12k$
$k + 4k + 9k + 12k = 1$, giving $k = \frac{1}{26}$

x	1	2	3	4
$P(X = x)$	$\frac{1}{26}$	$\frac{4}{26}$	$\frac{9}{26}$	$\frac{12}{26}$

(b) $P(X < 3) = \frac{1}{26} + \frac{4}{26} = \frac{5}{26}$

2 (a)

y	1	2	3	4	5
$P(Y = y)$	$\frac{5}{35}$	$\frac{8}{35}$	$\frac{9}{35}$	$\frac{8}{35}$	$\frac{5}{35}$

(b) $P(Y \geqslant 3) = \frac{9}{35} + \frac{8}{35} + \frac{5}{35} = \frac{22}{35}$ (or $1 - (\frac{5}{35} + \frac{8}{35}) = \frac{22}{35}$)

3 (a) $a = 0.2$

w	-4	-1	0	1	3	6
$P(W = w)$	0.15	0.4	0.2	0.05	0.1	0.1

(b) $P(2W + 5 \geqslant 4) = 0.45$

75. The binomial distribution

1 (a) Any two reasons from the following: fixed number of trials; two outcomes (allergic or not); fixed probabilities; independent trials.

(b) $P(X = 2) = \binom{40}{2} \times (0.05)^2 \times (0.95)^{38} = 0.278$ (3 s.f.)

(c) 0.677 (3 s.f.)

2 (a) 0.068 (3 s.f.)   (b) 0.805 (3 s.f.)

3 The probability of picking a toffee is not fixed at 0.5.

4 (a) 0.237 (3 s.f.)   (b) 0.213 (3 s.f.)

(c) 0.764 (3 s.f.)

76. Hypothesis testing

1 $P(X \leqslant 7) = 0.886$, $P(X \geqslant 8) = 1 - 0.886 = 0.114$
Since $0.114 > 0.10$, there is not enough evidence to reject H_0
So the conclusion is that the dice is not biased towards 1

2 $H_0: p = 0.55$, $H_1: p > 0.55$; $X \sim B(18, 0.55)$
$P(X \geqslant 14) = 1 - P(X \leqslant 13) = 0.041$
$0.041 < 0.05$, so reject H_0 and accept H_1
The probability is higher than 0.55, so the striker has underestimated his chances of scoring.

3 H_0: $p = 0.519$, H_1: $p \neq 0.519$; $X \sim B(50, 0.519)$
$np = 50 \times 0.519 \approx 26$ and since $19 < 26$ calculate $P(X \leq 19)$
Two-tailed test, so test $P(X \leq 19)$ at the 2.5% significance level.
$P(X \leq 19) = 0.034$
$0.034 > 0.025$ so there is not enough evidence to reject H_0. There is no evidence to suggest that this result is different from the UK average.

77. Critical regions

G 1 Model this by $X \sim B(30, 0.2)$
H_0: $p = 0.2$; H_1: $p \neq 0.2$ (two-tailed test)
$P(X \leq 2) = 0.044 < 0.05$
$P(X \leq 3) = 0.123 > 0.05$
$P(X \geq 11) = 0.026 < 0.05$
$P(X \geq 10) = 0.061 > 0.05$
The critical region is $X \leq 2$ and $X \geq 11$
So catching fewer than 3 or more than 10 dark moths would indicate that pollution levels are changing.

2 (a) H_0: $p = 0.22$ H_1: $p > 0.22$
$P(X \geq 14) = 0.041 < 0.05$, $P(X \geq 13) = 0.083 > 0.05$
Critical region is $X \geq 14$

(b) 0.041 or 4.1%

(c) 12 is not in the critical region so this is insufficient to reject H_0 at the 5% significance level.

3 (a) $P(X \leq 20) = 0.018 < 0.025$, $P(X \leq 21) = 0.040 > 0.25$
$P(X \geq 31) = 0.050 > 0.025$, $P(X \geq 32) = 0.019 < 0.25$
Critical region is $X \leq 20$ and $X \geq 32$

(b) $0.018 + 0.019 = 0.037$ or 3.7%

(c) 19 is in the critical region so reject H_0 at the 5% significance level.

78. You are the examiner!

1 (a) Stratified sampling

(b) Total = 162, 15% of 162 rounds to 24 vehicles for the sample
Large-load vehicles = $0.15 \times 3 = 0.45 \rightarrow 1$ vehicle
Light vans = $0.15 \times 135 = 20.25 \rightarrow 20$ vehicles
Company cars = $0.15 \times 24 = 3.6 \rightarrow 3$ vehicles
(to make a total of 24)

2 (a) x values are:

30   37   45   46   48   50   51   51   56   60

Median = 49; IQR = $51 - 45 = 6$

(b) $3 \times$ IQR = $3 \times 6 = 18$, $49 - 18 = 31$ and 30 is lower than this, so 30 is an outlier

(c) It is not unusual for a team to score quite a lot of goals but not win many games (probably quite a few narrow defeats) and so only score a relatively low number of points so we retain the data for team F

(d)
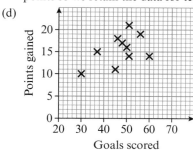

(e) Positive correlation which implies that the more goals you score, the more points you gain.

79. You are the examiner!

3 (a) Mean = $-88 \div 20 = -4.4\,$cm
SD = $\sqrt{4292 \div 20 - (4.4)^2} = 13.97\,$cm

(b) Mean = $100\,$m $- 4.4\,$cm $= 99.96\,$m (2 d.p.)
SD = $0.1397\,$m = $0.14\,$m (2 d.p.)

(c) New mean = $-50 \div 19 = -2.63\,$cm,
new $\Sigma x^2 = 4292 - 38^2 = 2848$
New SD = $\sqrt{2848 \div 19 - (2.63)^2} = 11.96$
New mean = $100\,$m $- 2.63\,$cm $= 99.97\,$m (2 d.p.)
New SD = $0.1196\,$m = $0.12\,$m (2 d.p.)

4 (a)
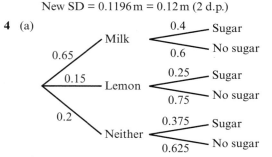

(b) P(does not take sugar) = $(0.65 \times 0.6) + (0.15 \times 0.75)$
$+ (0.2 \times 0.625)$
$= 0.39 + 0.1125 + 0.125$
$= 0.6275$

MECHANICS

80. Modelling in mechanics

1 (a) There is no friction.

(b) It has no weight.

(c) Acceleration is the same for both particles.

(d) Tension in the string is the same throughout its length.

(e) Each weight acts at a single point.

2 The string is light and inextensible, so the tension is the same throughout; the mass can be modelled as a particle, ignore any rotation of the mass; there is no air resistance and the motion will take place along the arc of a circle.

3 (a) 12.4 m   (b) 88.9 m   (c) 17.8 m

(d) The ball is modelled as a particle and there is no air resistance to the motion.

81. Motion graphs

G 1 (a) $v\,(\mathrm{m\,s^{-1}})$

(b) Area = Area 1 + Area 2 + Area 3
$= (30 \times 40) + (20 \times 60) + (\frac{1}{2} \times 10 \times x) = 2500$
$1200 + 1200 + 5x = 2500$
$x = \frac{100}{5} = 20$
Deceleration = $\frac{10}{20} = 0.5\,\mathrm{m\,s^{-2}}$

2 (a) $v\,(\mathrm{m\,s^{-1}})$

(b) 80 m   (c) 35 s

82. Constant acceleration 1

⟨G⟩ 1 (a) $s = ?$ $u = 5$ $v = 20$ $a = ?$ $t = 4$

$v = u + at$

$20 = 5 + a \times 4$ $4a = 15$ $a = 3.75\,\text{m s}^{-2}$

(b) $s = ?$ $u = 5$ $v = 20$ $a = 3.75$ $t = 4$

$s = \frac{1}{2}(5 + 20) \times 4 = 50\,\text{m}$

2 (a) $1.8\,\text{m s}^{-2}$ (b) $4.375\,\text{m}$

3 (a) $a = -1.\dot{3}\,\text{m s}^{-2}$ (deceleration $= 1.\dot{3}\,\text{m s}^{-2}$)   (b) $600\,\text{m}$

83. Constant acceleration 2

⟨G⟩ 1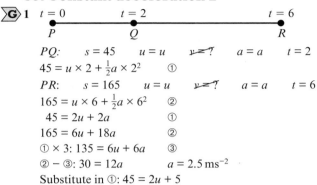

PQ: $s = 45$ $u = u$ $v = ?$ $a = a$ $t = 2$

$45 = u \times 2 + \frac{1}{2}a \times 2^2$ ①

PR: $s = 165$ $u = u$ $v = ?$ $a = a$ $t = 6$

$165 = u \times 6 + \frac{1}{2}a \times 6^2$ ②

$45 = 2u + 2a$ ①

$165 = 6u + 18a$ ②

① $\times$ 3: $135 = 6u + 6a$ ③

② $-$ ③: $30 = 12a$ $a = 2.5\,\text{ms}^{-2}$

Substitute in ①: $45 = 2u + 5$

$2u = 40$

$u = 20\,\text{m s}^{-1}$

2 (a) $37.75\,\text{m s}^{-1}$

(b) $102\,\text{m}$

(c) $6\,\text{s}$

84. Motion under gravity

⟨G⟩ 1 (a) $s = ?$ $u = 21$ $v = 0$ $a = -9.8$ $t = ?$

$v^2 = u^2 + 2as$ so $0^2 = 21^2 - 2 \times 9.8 \times h$ $441 = 19.6h$

$h = 22.5\,\text{m}$

(b) $s = -1.5$ $u = 21$ $v = ?$ $a = -9.8$ $t = ?$

$v^2 = u^2 + 2as$, so $v^2 = 21^2 + 29.4 = 470.4$,

so $v = 21.69\,\text{m s}^{-1}$

(c) $s = ?$ $u = 21$ $v = -22$ $a = -9.8$ $t = ?$

$v = u + at$

$-22 = 21 - 9.8t$

$t = 4.39\,\text{s}$

⟨G⟩ 2 (a) $s = 50$ $u = 0$ $v = ?$ $a = a$ $t = 4$

$s = ut + \frac{1}{2}at^2$

$50 = 0 + \frac{1}{2}a \times 4^2$ $a = \frac{50}{8} = 6.25\,\text{m s}^{-2}$

(b) $v = u + at$

$v = 0 + 6.25 \times 4 = 25\,\text{m s}^{-1}$

(c) $s = ut + \frac{1}{2}at^2$

$s = 25 \times 3 - \frac{1}{2} \times 9.8 \times 9 = 30.9$

Total height $= 30.9 + 50 = 80.9\,\text{m}$

85. Forces

⟨G⟩ 1 (a)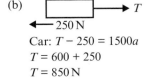

Van and car: $2750 - 900 - 250 = (2500 + 1500)a$

$1600 = 4000a$

$a = 0.4\,\text{m s}^{-2}$

(b)

Car: $T - 250 = 1500a$

$T = 600 + 250$

$T = 850\,\text{N}$

2 (a) $T = 12\,608 \approx 13\,000\,\text{N}$ (2 s.f.)

(b) $R = 663 \approx 660\,\text{N}$ (2 s.f.)

86. Forces as vectors

⟨G⟩ 1 (a)

$\tan\theta = \frac{1}{2}$; $\theta = 26.6°$

angle $= 90 + 26.6 = 116.6° \approx 117°$ (3 s.f.)

(b) $\mathbf{R} = (3\mathbf{i} - 6\mathbf{j}) + (p\mathbf{i} + q\mathbf{j})$

$= (3 + p)\mathbf{i} + (-6 + q)\mathbf{j}$

$3 + p = -2(-6 + q)$

$3 + p = 12 - 2q$

$p + 2q = 9$

2 (a) $63°$

(b) $p = -2$, $\mathbf{R} = -8\mathbf{j}\,\text{N}$

3 (a) $p = -4$ and $q = 6$

(b) Magnitude $= 9.22\,\text{N}$, angle $= 139.4°$

87. Motion in 2D

1 (a) $\dfrac{2\sqrt{13}}{5}\,\text{m s}^{-1}$ or $1.44\,\text{m s}^{-2}$ (3 s.f.)

(b) $146.3°$

⟨G⟩ 2 (a) $\mathbf{F} = m\mathbf{a}$

$4\mathbf{i} + 3\mathbf{j} = 0.5\mathbf{a}$

$\mathbf{a} = 8\mathbf{i} + 6\mathbf{j}$

$|a| = \sqrt{8^2 + 6^2} = 10\,\text{m s}^{-2}$

$s = ut + \frac{1}{2}at^2$

$= 0 + 0.5 \times 10 \times 5^2$

$= 125\,\text{m}$

(b) Resultant force $= 4\mathbf{i} + 3\mathbf{j} + 1.3\mathbf{i} - 0.5\mathbf{j} = (5.3\mathbf{i} + 2.5\mathbf{j})\,\text{N}$

$a = 11.7\,\text{ms}^2$ to 3 s.f.

3 $(2\mathbf{i} - 7\mathbf{j})\,\text{N}$

88. Pulleys

⟨G⟩ 1 (a) A: $4g - T = 4a$

$4g - \dfrac{16g}{7} = T$

$T = \dfrac{12g}{7}$ $(= 16.8 \approx 17\,\text{N})$

B: $T - mg = ma$

$\dfrac{12g}{7} = m\left(g + \dfrac{4g}{7}\right)$

$\dfrac{12g}{7} = \dfrac{11mg}{7}$

$m = 1.1\,\text{kg}$

(b) ($\uparrow$): $v = u + at = 0 + \dfrac{4g}{7} \times 0.5 = \dfrac{2g}{7} = 2.8\,\text{m s}^{-1}$

($\uparrow$): $s = ut + \frac{1}{2}at^2 = 0 + \frac{1}{2} \times \dfrac{4g}{7} \times 0.5^2 = 0.7$

($\downarrow$): $s = ut + \frac{1}{2}at^2 = 0.7 + 3 = 3.7$

$3.7 = -2.8t + 4.9t^2$

$4.9t^2 - 2.8t - 3.7 = 0$

$t = \dfrac{2.8 \pm \sqrt{2.8^2 + 4 \times 4.9 \times 3.7}}{9.8}$

$= 1.2\,\text{s}$

2 $a = 3.92\,\text{m s}^{-2}$, $T = 41.16\,\text{N}$

Answers

89. Connected particles

G **1** (a) $F = ma$ for A: $T = 4.8a$

$F = ma$ for B: $1.2g - T = 1.2a$

Adding gives $1.2g = 6$, so $a = 1.96\,\text{m s}^{-2}$

Substituting gives $T = 4.8 \times 1.96 = 9.408\,\text{N}$

(b) $s = 3 \quad u = 0 \quad v = ? \quad a = 1.96 \quad t = ?$

$v = 3.43\,\text{m s}^{-1}$

$t = 1.75\,\text{s}$

2 (a) $a = 1.4\,\text{m s}^{-2}$, v after $2.5\,\text{s} = 4.2\,\text{m s}^{-1}$ (then u for motion under gravity)

Further time = 0.43 s

(b) $s = 6.3\,\text{m}$ for connected particles, then $s = 0.9\,\text{m}$ for motion under gravity.

Total distance = 7.2 m

90. Combining techniques

1 (a) $a = 1.6\,\text{m s}^{-2}$

$m = 5.6875 \approx 5.7\,\text{kg}$ (2 s.f.)

(b) (i) The measured mass $m = 5\,\text{kg}$. This is smaller than the calculated mass $m = 5.7\,\text{kg}$. This suggests that the resistance is greater then 15.5 N.

(ii) Maybe the resistance should be modelled as a variable force.

91. Variable acceleration 1

G **1** (a) $s = t(t^2 - 11t + 24) = t(t - 3)(t - 8)$

$s = 0$ when $t = 3$ and when $t = 8$

Graph crosses t-axis at t = 0, $t = 3$, $t = 8$

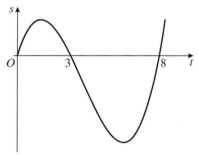

(b) Moves in positive direction from O then changes direction and passes O after $3\,\text{s}$, continues in negative direction until changes direction again and returns to O after $8\,\text{s}$.

(c) Differentiate to get $v = 3t^2 - 22t + 24$

Equate to zero to get $t = \frac{4}{3}$ and $t = 6$

(d) $t = \frac{4}{3}$ gives $s = 14.8$ and $t = 6$ gives $s = -36$

so 36 m from O in negative direction

2 (a) $t^3 - 24t^2 + 144t = t(t^2 - 24t + 144) = t(t - 12)^2$

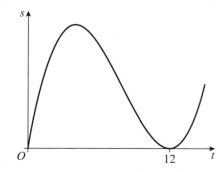

(b) $v = 16\,\text{m s}^{-1}$ \qquad (c) $t = 4\,\text{s}$ and $t = 12\,\text{s}$

(d) This is when $t = 4$, $s = 28.44\,\text{m}$

92. Variable acceleration 2

G **1** (a) P is instantaneously at rest when $v = 0$

$t^2 - 8t + 12 = 0$, $(t - 2)(t - 6) = 0$, so $t = 2$ and $t = 6$

(b) $t = 4$ gives $v = -4$

so max is $v = 12$ when $t = 0$

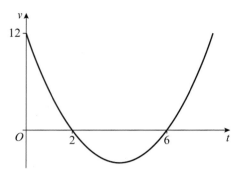

(c) $\int_0^2 v\,dt$ to $\int_2^5 v\,dt$

total distance $= 19\frac{2}{3}\,\text{m}$

2 (a) $8\,\text{m s}^{-1}$

(b) $v = 8 - 2t^2 = 2(2 + t)(2 - t)$

Instantaneously at rest when $t = 2$

(c) At $t = 0$, $s = 0$; at $t = 2$, $s = 10\frac{2}{3}$; at $t = 4$, $s = -10\frac{2}{3}$

Total distance $= 3 \times 10\frac{2}{3} = 32\,\text{m}$

93. Deriving *suvat* equations

G **1** (a) Distance travelled s = area under graph

so $s = A_1 + A_2$

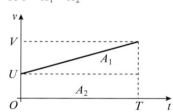

$A_1 = \frac{1}{2} \times \text{base} \times \text{height} = \frac{1}{2} \times T \times (V - U)$

$A_2 = U \times T$

So $s = \frac{1}{2}T(V - U) + UT = \frac{1}{2}TV - \frac{1}{2}TU + UT$

$= \frac{1}{2}UT + \frac{1}{2}VT = \left(\dfrac{U + V}{2}\right)T$ as required

(b) (i) $s = \frac{1}{2}T(U + V)$

$s = \frac{1}{2}T(U + U + AT)$

$s = \frac{1}{2}T(2U + AT) = UT + \frac{1}{2}aT^2$

(ii) $s = \frac{1}{2}T(U + V) = \dfrac{(V - U)(V + U)}{2a}$, since $T = \dfrac{(V - U)}{a}$

$s = \dfrac{(V^2 - U^2)}{2a}$, so $2as = V^2 - U^2$ and $V^2 = U^2 + 2as$ as required

2 (a) $v = \int 0.8\,dt = 0.8t + c$

$v = 5$ when $t = 0$, so $c = 5$ and $v = 0.8t + 5$

$s = \int v\,dt = 0.4t^2 + 5t + k$

$s = 0$ when $t = 0$, so $k = 0$ and $s = 0.4t^2 + 5t$

(b) $16t - 0.3t^2 + 0.4t^2 + 5t = 720$

$0.1t^2 + 21t - 720 = 0$

$t^2 + 210t - 7200 = 0$

$(t - 30)(t + 240) = 0$

$t = 30$

(c) When $t = 30$, $s = 16 \times 30 - 0.3 \times 900$

$= 480 - 270 = 210\,\text{m}$ from A

94. You are the examiner!

1 (a)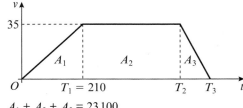

$A_1 + A_2 + A_3 = 23\,100$

$A_3 = 1575$

(b) $A_1 = \frac{1}{2} \times 210 \times 35 = 3675$,

so $A_2 = 23\,100 - 3675 - 1575 = 17\,850$

$A_2 = (T_2 - 210) \times 35 = 17\,850$,

so $(T_2 - 210) = 17\,850 \div 35 = 510$, so $T_2 = 720$

$A_3 = \frac{1}{2} \times (T_3 - 720) \times 35 = 1575$,

so $(T_3 - 720) = 3150 \div 35 = 90$, so $T_3 = 810$

Time for the whole journey = 810 seconds

= 13.5 minutes

2 (a) $\mathbf{F}_1 + \mathbf{F}_2 + \mathbf{F}_3 = 0$ since the forces are in equilibrium

$(2p\mathbf{i} - \mathbf{j}) + (q\mathbf{i} - 5p\mathbf{j}) + 4\mathbf{i} - 7q\mathbf{j} = \mathbf{0}$

Sum of **i**-component coefficients = 0

Sum of **j**-component coefficients = 0

So $2p + q + 4 = 0$ and $-1 - 5p - 7q = 0$

(simultaneous equations)

Multiply $(2p + q = -4) \times 7$: $14p + 7q = -28$

Subtracting gives $9p = -27$ so $p = -3$

Substituting gives $q = 2$

(b) $\mathbf{F}_1 = (-6\mathbf{i} - \mathbf{j})\,\text{N}$ and $\mathbf{F}_2 = (2\mathbf{i} + 15\mathbf{j})\,\text{N}$

so $\mathbf{R} = \mathbf{F}_1 + \mathbf{F}_2 = -4\mathbf{i} + 14\mathbf{j}\,\text{N}$

Magnitude of $\mathbf{R} = \sqrt{4^2 + 14^2} = \sqrt{212} = 14.56\,\text{N}$

Angle with **j**: $\tan\theta = \frac{4}{14}$ so $\theta = 15.9° \approx 16°$

3 (a) Apply $F = ma$ to both particles and solve simultaneously:

$6g - T = 6a$

$T - 4g = 4a$

$2g = 10a$

$a = \frac{g}{5} = 1.96\,\text{m s}^{-2}$

$T = 4a + 4g = 4(a + g) = 4(1.96 + 9.8)$

$= 47.04\,\text{N}$

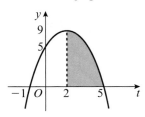

(b) Using $v = u + at$, $v = 0 + 1.96 \times 1.5 = 2.94\,\text{m s}^{-1}$

(c) A now moves under gravity with initial speed $2.94\,\text{m s}^{-1}$

Using $v = u + at$, $0 = 2.94 - 9.8t$, $t = 2.94 \div 9.8 = 0.3\,\text{s}$

(d) When connected, using $s = ut + \frac{1}{2}at^2$

$s = 0 + \frac{1}{2} \times 1.96 \times 1.5^2 = 2.205\,\text{m}$

When moving under gravity, using $v^2 = u^2 + 2as$

$0 = 2.94^2 - 2 \times 9.8 \times s$

$s = 2.94^2 \div 19.6 = 0.441\,\text{m}$

Total distance travelled by particle $A = 2.205 + 0.441$

$= 2.646\,\text{m}$

4 (a) $v = \int a\,\mathrm{d}t = \int (4 - 2t)\,\mathrm{d}t = 4t - t^2 + c$

When $t = 0$, $v = 5$, giving $c = 5$

$v = 5 + 4t - t^2$

(b) Greatest speed is when $a = 0$, $4 - 2t = 0$, $t = 2$

$v_{\max} = 5 + 8 - 4 = 9\,\text{m s}^{-1}$

(c) A v–t sketch graph is useful here.

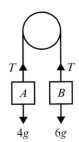

For instantaneous rest, $v = 0$

$5 + 4t - t^2 = 0$

$(5 - t)(1 + t) = 0$

$t = 5$ or $t = -1$ (inadmissible)

Distance (shaded area) $= \int_2^5 (5 + 4t - t^2)\,\mathrm{d}t$

$= \left[5t + 2t^2 - \frac{t^3}{3}\right]_2^5$

$= (25 + 50 - \frac{125}{3}) - (10 + 8 - \frac{8}{3})$

$= 33\frac{1}{3} - 15\frac{1}{3}$

$= 18\,\text{m}$

Practice Paper 1

Pure Mathematics

1 $32^{4x+1} = (2^5)^{4x+1} = 2^{20x+5} = 2^y$

$y = 20x + 5$

2 (a) $\overrightarrow{AB} = \overrightarrow{AO} + \overrightarrow{OB} = 3\mathbf{i} - 2\mathbf{j} + 4\mathbf{i} + 6\mathbf{j} = 7\mathbf{i} + 4\mathbf{j}$

(b) $|\overrightarrow{AB}| = \sqrt{7^2 + 4^2} = \sqrt{49 + 16} = \sqrt{65}$

3 $2x^2 + x > 28$

$2x^2 + x - 28 > 0$

$(2x - 7)(x + 4) > 0$

$x < -4$ and $x > 3.5$

4 $\dfrac{40 - \sqrt{180}}{4\sqrt{5} - 3} = \dfrac{40 - 6\sqrt{5}}{4\sqrt{5} - 3} \times \dfrac{4\sqrt{5} + 3}{4\sqrt{5} + 3}$

$= \dfrac{160\sqrt{5} - 120 + 120 - 18\sqrt{5}}{80 - 9} = \dfrac{142\sqrt{5}}{71} = 2\sqrt{5}$

or

(e.g.) $\dfrac{40 - \sqrt{180}}{4\sqrt{5} - 3} = \dfrac{40 - 6\sqrt{5}}{4\sqrt{5} - 3} = \dfrac{\sqrt{5}(8\sqrt{5} - 6)}{4\sqrt{5} - 3} = 2\sqrt{5}$

5 $\displaystyle\int_1^{\sqrt{2}} \left(4x^2 - 1 - \frac{2}{x^3}\right)\mathrm{d}x = \left[\frac{4x^3}{3} - x + \frac{1}{x^2}\right]_1^{\sqrt{2}}$

$= \left[\frac{8\sqrt{2}}{3} - \sqrt{2} + \frac{1}{2}\right] - \left[\frac{4}{3} - 1 + 1\right]$

$= \frac{5\sqrt{2}}{3} - \frac{5}{6} = \frac{5}{6}(2\sqrt{2} - 1)$

6 $f(x) = 4x^2 + 7x$

$f'(x) = \lim\limits_{h \to 0} \dfrac{f(x + h) - f(x)}{h}$

$= \lim\limits_{h \to 0} \dfrac{4(x + h)^2 + 7(x + h) - 4x^2 - 7x}{h}$

$= \lim\limits_{h \to 0} \dfrac{4x^2 + 8xh + 4h^2 + 7x + 7h - 4x^2 - 7x}{h}$

$= \lim\limits_{h \to 0} (8x + 4h + 7)$

As $h \to 0$, $4h \to 0$ so $f'(x) = 8x + 7$

7 $\dfrac{\sin A}{5} = \dfrac{\sin 70°}{7}$

$\sin A = \dfrac{5\sin 70°}{7}$, so $A = 42.16...°$

$B = 180° - 70° - 42.16...°$

$= 67.839...°$

Area $= \frac{1}{2} \times 5 \times 7 \times \sin 67.839...° = 16.2\,\text{cm}^2$ (3 s.f.)

8 $5\sin(x - 45°) = 2$, so $\sin(x - 45°) = 0.4$
$-180° \leqslant x \leqslant 180°$, $-225° \leqslant (x - 45°) \leqslant 135°$
Principal value of $\sin(x - 45°) = 0.4$ is $23.6°$
$x - 45° = -203.6°$ and $23.6°$
$x = -158.6°$ and $68.6°$

9 $f(x) = 3x^3 + 2x^2 - 23x + k$

(a) If $(x + 2)$ is a factor, $f(-2) = 0$
So $3(-2)^3 + 2(-2)^2 - 23(-2) + k = 0$
$-24 + 8 + 46 + k = 0$
$k = -30$

(b) $3x^3 + 2x^2 - 23x - 30 = (x + 2)(ax^2 + bx + c)$
By inspection, $ax^3 = 3x^3$ and $c = -15$
So $3x^3 + 2x^2 - 23x - 30 = (x + 2)(3x^2 + bx - 15)$
Comparing x^2 coefficients: $2 = 6 + b$, so $b = -4$
Hence, $f(x) = (x + 2)(3x^2 - 4x - 15)$
$= (x + 2)(3x + 5)(x - 3)$

10 (a) $\left(1 - \dfrac{x}{3}\right)^9 \approx 1 + 9\left(\dfrac{-x}{3}\right) + \dfrac{9.8}{1.2}\left(\dfrac{-x}{3}\right)^2 + \dfrac{9.8.7}{1.2.3}\left(\dfrac{-x}{3}\right)^3$
$= 1 - 3x + 4x^2 - \dfrac{28}{9}x^3$

(b) $1 - \dfrac{x}{3} = 0.996$, $\dfrac{x}{3} = 0.004$, $x = 0.012$
So $(0.996)^9 \approx 1 - 3(0.012) + 4(0.012)^2 - \dfrac{28}{9}(0.012)^3$
$= 0.964570$
$= 0.9646$ (4 d.p.)

11 (a) Centre is $(5, -4)$

(b) Gradient from centre to $(-3, 2) = \dfrac{-3}{4}$
Gradient of tangent $= \dfrac{4}{3}$, equation is $y - 2 = \dfrac{4}{3}(x + 3)$
i.e. $4x - 3y + 18 = 0$
P is $(-4.5, 0)$ and Q is $(0, 6)$
Area $\triangle POQ = \dfrac{1}{2} \times 4.5 \times 6 = 13.5$ units of area

12 (a) $2\log_2(x - 4) - \log_2(3x - 4) = \log_2 2$
$\log_2(x - 4)^2 - \log_2(3x - 4) = \log_2 2$
$\log_2 \dfrac{(x - 4)^2}{(3x - 4)} = \log_2 2$
So $\dfrac{(x - 4)^2}{(3x - 4)} = 2$, i.e. $x^2 - 8x + 16 = 6x - 8$
i.e. $x^2 - 14x + 24 = 0$

(b) $x^2 - 14x + 24 = 0$, $(x - 12)(x - 2) = 0$
i.e. $x = 12$ or $x = 2$
$x = 2$ is inadmissible since $\log_2(x - 4)$ must be such that $(x - 4) > 0$
So the only solution is $x = 12$

13 (a) L_1 is $3y + 5x - 4 = 0$, i.e. $y = \dfrac{-5}{3}x + \dfrac{4}{3}$
So gradient L_1 is $\dfrac{-5}{3}$ and gradient L_2 is $\dfrac{3}{5}$
Equation L_2 is $y - 6 = \dfrac{3}{5}(x + 2)$, i.e. $3x - 5y + 36 = 0$

(b) L_2 crosses the x-axis when $y = 0$, i.e. $x = -12$
So B is $(-12, 0)$ and the length $AB = \sqrt{10^2 + 6^2} = \sqrt{136}$

14 $y = 5x - k$ is a tangent to $y = kx^2 - 7x + 5$
Solving these simultaneously will have only one x value, from $b^2 - 4ac = 0$
$kx^2 - 7x + 5 = 5x - k$
$kx^2 - 12x + (5 + k) = 0$
$b^2 - 4ac = 0$, so $12^2 - 4 \times k \times (5 + k) = 0$
So $144 - 20k - 4k^2 = 0$
i.e. $k^2 + 5k - 36 = 0$
$(k + 9)(k - 4) = 0$
$k = -9$, $k = 4$

15 (a)

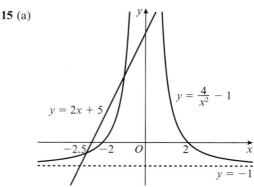

(b) $x = 0$ (y-axis) and $y = -1$

(c) $\dfrac{4}{x^2} - 1 = 2x + 5$
$4 - x^2 = 2x^3 + 5x^2$
$0 = 2x^3 + 6x^2 - 4$
$0 = (x + 1)(x^2 + 2x - 2)$
x coordinates at points of intersection are $x = -1$ and $x = -1 \pm \sqrt{3}$

16 (a)

Volume = 20 litres = $20\,000\,\text{cm}^3$
$2x^2y = 20\,000$
$y = \dfrac{10\,000}{x^2}$
$A = 2(2x^2 + 2xy + xy) = 4x^2 + 6xy = 4x^2 + \dfrac{60\,000}{x}$

(b) $\dfrac{dA}{dx} = 8x - \dfrac{60\,000}{x^2}$, zero when $x^3 = \dfrac{60\,000}{8} = 7500$
So $x = \sqrt[3]{7500} = 19.574\ldots$
So $A = 4(19.574\ldots)^2 + \dfrac{60\,000}{19.574\ldots} = 4600\,\text{cm}^2$ (3 s.f.)

(c) $\dfrac{d^2 A}{dx^2} = 8 + \dfrac{120\,000}{x^3} = 24$ which is > 0 when $x^3 = 7500$,
$x = 19.574\ldots$
So the value of A ($4600\,\text{cm}^2$) is a minimum.

Practice Paper 2
Statistics and Mechanics
Section A: Statistics

1 (a) (i) 26 cm is within the range of the data so this estimate will be reliable (interpolation).

(ii) 30 cm is outside the range of the data so this estimate will be unreliable (extrapolation).

(b) h is the dependent variable. The regression equation cannot be used to predict the value of l, the independent variable.

2 $\bar{x} = (62.1 + 15) \div 13 = 59.3$ (3 s.f.)
Standard deviation = $6.17 \div 1.3 = 4.75$ (3 s.f.)

3 (a) $P(C) = 2 \times P(A)$, so $p + q = 2(p + 0.08) \Rightarrow q = p + 0.16$
Total probability = 1, so $2p + q + 0.08 + 0.14 + 0.26 = 1$
i.e. $2p + q + 0.52$
Solving simultaneously
$2p + (p + 0.16) = 0.52$
giving $p = 0.12$ and $q = 0.28$

(b) $P(B) = 0.08 + 0.14 + 0.12 = 0.34$
$P(C) = p + q = 0.4$
$P(B) \times P(C) = 0.34 \times 0.4 = 0.136$
$P(B \text{ and } C) = p = 0.12$, so B and C are not statistically independent.

4 (a)

Time, t (minutes)	Number of runners	Frequency density
$65 < t \leqslant 70$	7	1.4
$70 < t \leqslant 80$	20	2.0
$80 < t \leqslant 90$	31	3.1
$90 < t \leqslant 105$	45	3.0
$105 < t \leqslant 120$	12	0.8
	115	

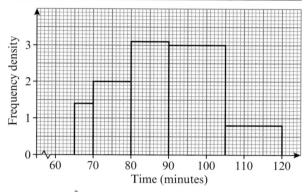

(b) 76 to 80 = $\frac{2}{5}$ of 20 = 8
80 to 105 = 31 + 45 = 76
76 to 80 = $\frac{1}{3}$ of 12 = 4
8 + 76 + 4 = 88
Percentage = $\frac{88}{115} \times 100 = 76.5\%$ (3 s.f.)

5 (a) B(24, 0.25)   P($X < 6$) = 0.422

(b) P($X < 4$) = 0.11501...
P($X < 10$) = 0.94533...
So P($4 \leqslant X < 10$) = 0.94533... − 0.11501... = 0.830

(c) Use B(20, 0.25)
H_0: P = 0.25
H_1: P > 0.25 (one-tail test)
P($X \geqslant 8$) = 0.101811...
0.101811... > 0.05 so there is insufficient evidence to reject H_0, so there is insufficient evidence to support the theory that more than 25% of people eat at least five portions of fruit and veg every day.

Section B: Mechanics

6 (a)

Distance = 14 m

(b) $T = \frac{14}{20} = 0.7$
Distance after brakes are applied = $\frac{1}{2} \times 20 \times (3.9 - 0.7)$
= 32 m
Total distance = 14 + 32 = 46 m

(c) Deceleration = $\frac{20}{3.2} = 6.25 \, \text{m s}^{-2}$

7 $a = 2t + 2.5$ $v = \int(2t + 2.5) \, \text{d}t = t^2 + 2.5t + c$
When $t = 0$, $v = 3$, so $c = 3$, hence $v = t^2 + 2.5t + 3$
When $t = T$, $v = 9$ so $9 = T^2 + 2.5T + 3$
i.e. $T^2 + 2.5T - 6 = 0$ i.e. $2T^2 + 5T - 12 = 0$
$(2T - 3)(T + 4) = 0$, so $T = 1.5 \, \text{s}$ ($T \neq -4$)

8 (a) $s = -h$ $u = u$ $v = -10.8$ $a = -9.8$ $t = 1.5$
$v = u + at$ gives $-10.8 = u - 9.8 \times 1.5$
$u = 14.7 - 10.8 = 3.9$

(b) $s = ut + \frac{1}{2}at^2$ gives $-h = 3.9 \times 1.5 - \frac{1}{2} \times 9.8 \times 1.5^2$
$-h = 5.85 - 11.025$, so $h = 5.175 = 5.18$ or 5.2

(c) The ball is modelled as a particle. Air resistance is neglected.

9 (a) For the trailer:
$u = 18$ $v = 0$ $s = ?$ $t = 3.2$ $a = ?$
Using $v = u + at$, $0 = 18 + a \times 3.2$, so $a = -5.625$
The deceleration of the trailer is $5.625 \, \text{m s}^{-2}$

(b) Using $F = ma$ for the trailer:
$-1260 = m \times -5.625$, giving $m = 224$
The trailer has a mass of 224 kg

(c) Using $F = ma$ for the whole system, when the truck and trailer were accelerating:
$6000 - 1260 - 3.8x = (3800 + 224) \times 0.55$
where $3.8x$ is the resistance on the truck.
i.e. $4740 - 3.8x = 2213.2$
So $x = (4740 - 2213.2) \div 3.8 = 664.947$
The resistance on the truck is 665 N per tonne.

Notes

Notes

Notes

Notes

Notes

Notes

Published by Pearson Education Limited, 80 Strand, London, WC2R 0RL.

www.pearsonschoolsandfecolleges.co.uk

Copies of official specifications for all Pearson qualifications may be found on the website: qualifications.pearson.com

Text and illustrations © Pearson Education Ltd 2018
Typeset and illustrated by Techset
Produced by ProjectOne
Cover illustration by Miriam Sturdee

The right of Glyn Payne to be identified as author of this work has been asserted by him in accordance with the Copyright, Designs and Patents Act 1988.

First published 2018

21 20 19
10 9 8 7 6 5 4 3

British Library Cataloguing in Publication Data
A catalogue record for this book is available from the British Library

ISBN 978 1 292 19061 7

Printed in Slovakia by Neografia

Notes from the publisher

1. While the publishers have made every attempt to ensure that advice on the qualification and its assessment is accurate, the official specification and associated assessment guidance materials are the only authoritative source of information and should always be referred to for definitive guidance.

Pearson examiners have not contributed to any sections in this resource relevant to examination papers for which they have responsibility.

2. Pearson has robust editorial processes, including answer and fact checks, to ensure the accuracy of the content in this publication, and every effort is made to ensure this publication is free of errors. We are, however, only human, and occasionally errors do occur. Pearson is not liable for any misunderstandings that arise as a result of errors in this publication, but it is our priority to ensure that the content is accurate. If you spot an error, please do contact us at resourcescorrections@pearson.com so we can make sure it is corrected.